Issues in Data Synthesis

William H. Yeaton, Paul M. Wortman, *Editors*

NEW DIRECTIONS FOR PROGRAM EVALUATION
A Publication of the Evaluation Research Society
ERNEST R. HOUSE, *Editor-in-Chief*

Number 24, December 1984

Paperback sourcebooks in
The Jossey-Bass Higher Education and
Social and Behavioral Sciences Series

Jossey-Bass Inc., Publishers
San Francisco • Washington • London

William H. Yeaton, Paul M. Wortman, (Eds.).
Issues in Data Synthesis.
New Directions for Program Evaluation, no. 24.
San Francisco: Jossey-Bass, 1984.

New Directions for Program Evaluation Series
A Publication of the Evaluation Research Society
Ernest R. House, *Editor-in-Chief*

New Directions for Program Evaluation (publication number
USPS 449-050) is published quarterly by Jossey-Bass Inc.,
Publishers, and is sponsored by the Evaluation Research Society.
Second-class postage rates paid at San Francisco, California,
and at additional mailing offices.

Correspondence:
Subscriptions, single-issue orders, change of address notices, undelivered
copies, and other correspondence should be sent to Subscriptions,
Jossey-Bass Inc., Publishers, 433 California Street, San Francisco
California 94104.

Editorial correspondence should be sent to the Editor-in-Chief,
Ernest House, CIRCE-270, Education Building, University of Illinois,
Champaign, Ill. 61820.

Library of Congress Catalogue Card Number LC 83-82738

International Standard Serial Number ISSN 0164-7989

International Standard Book Number ISBN 87589-785-1

Cover art by Willi Baum

Manufactured in the United States of America

Ordering Information

The paperback sourcebooks listed below are published quarterly and can be ordered either by subscription or single-copy.

Subscriptions cost $35.00 per year for institutions, agencies, and libraries. Individuals can subscribe at the special rate of $25.00 per year *if payment is by personal check*. (Note that the full rate of $35.00 applies if payment is by institutional check, even if the subscription is designated for an individual.) Standing orders are accepted. Subscriptions normally begin with the first of the four sourcebooks in the current publication year of the series. When ordering, please indicate if you prefer your subscription to begin with the first issue of the *coming* year.

Single copies are available at $8.95 when payment accompanies order, and *all single-copy orders under $25.00 must include payment*. (California, New Jersey, New York, and Washington, D.C., residents please include appropriate sales tax.) For billed orders, cost per copy is $8.95 plus postage and handling. (Prices subject to change without notice.)

Bulk orders (ten or more copies) of any individual sourcebook are available at the following discounted prices: 10–49 copies, $8.05 each; 50–100 copies, $7.15 each; over 100 copies, *inquire*. Sales tax and postage and handling charges apply as for single copy orders.

To ensure correct and prompt delivery, all orders must give either the *name of an individual* or an *official purchase order number*. Please submit your order as follows:

Subscriptions: specify series and year subscription is to begin.
Single Copies: specify sourcebook code (such as, PE8) and first two words of title.

Mail orders for United States and Possessions, Latin America, Canada, Japan, Australia, and New Zealand to:
Jossey-Bass Inc., Publishers
433 California Street
San Francisco, California 94104

Mail orders for all other parts of the world to:
Jossey-Bass Limited
28 Banner Street
London EC1Y 8QE

New Directions for Program Evaluation Series
Ernest R. House, *Editor-in-Chief*

Contents

Editors' Notes

Our thinking about research synthesis has been influenced by our interest in assessment of medical technology. In fact, we have found it useful to think about recent developments in research synthesis as changes in a new technology. Certainly, the rapid dissemination of research synthesis parallels the rapid dissemination of new medical technologies. Moreover, synthesis promises to increase use of research and to make program evaluation a more cumulative activity. But, just as many new medical technologies have negative side effects, are prohibitively expensive, and eventually prove to be ineffective, so, too, the path of research synthesis may lead to the dead end that many good ideas seem to have reached. Nevertheless, the analogy reveals dimensions to research synthesis that predict many useful applications for evaluators.

For example, new medical technologies are often first tested on a relatively homogeneous group of persons. Thus, total hip replacement was at first largely restricted to the elderly. But, as the method of producing a viable hip socket was refined and as friction was minimalized, the procedure has been extended to younger patients. Similarly, the groups that use research synthesis procedures are beginning to diversify. For example, in Chapter Five of this volume, Eleanor Chelimsky and Linda G. Morra illustrate evaluation synthesis, a novel variation developed by the U.S. General Accounting Office (GAO) for summarizing evaluative evidence. Congress uses the results of evaluation synthesis in establishing new policies or in altering existing policies.

New medical procedures often go through protracted transition periods as increasing numbers of physicians gain experience with them. For example, chemotherapy regimens have changed considerably since evidence of their effectiveness in the treatment of cancer was first presented. Similarly, data synthesis procedures are refined, and alternative procedures are created. In Chapter Two, Larry V. Hedges outlines the development of some statistical analysis procedures that go beyond those available just a few years ago, and in Chapter Four, Richard J. Light shows that the research synthesis technique can be expanded to allow very specific conclusions about interaction effects.

Most new medical technologies are limited to investigations that ask specific questions and that focus on specific parts of the body. In time, research questions become more complex, and the relevant areas of the body can change. Early use of computerized tomography (CT) scans was limited to the brain, but in recent years, CT scans have been used to study many other portions of the human anatomy, including the liver and the kidney. In much the same way, the areas in which research synthesis is being applied are changing rapidly. In Chapter One, Fred B. Bryant and Paul M. Wortman show how the technique has been used to evaluate the effects of desegregation in public schools. In Chapter Three, William H. Yeaton and Paul M. Wortman apply synthesis methods to medical problems, and in Chapter Five Eleanor Chelimsky and Linda G. Morra demonstrate its utility in the assessment of social programs.

New medical procedures are often overused. For example, many physicians argue that antibiotics are overprescribed, and considerable controversy surrounds the most suitable set of patient symptoms that indicate coronary artery bypass graft surgery. We anticipate similar problems with research synthesis as the limits of its applicability are tested. For example, we can ask whether meaningful research synthesis can be conducted with quasi-experimental designs or with designs that do not use a control group. Further, if we decide to admit such designs to our syntheses, we can ask whether all such studies should be included. Few researchers have addressed these questions as yet, but it seems inevitable that syntheses of studies that use each person as his or her own control will eventually be attempted. These questions have great importance for evaluators, since the literature that they encounter is often flawed. The authors of Chapter One address problems raised by attempts to synthesize quasi-experiments.

New technologies, whether they be medical technologies or research synthesis, must either reflect the kinds of questions that a research field is currently asking, or they must provide users with a vehicle for asking new questions. Microscopes allowed us to look at the world in different ways and to ask fundamentally different questions. Likewise, research synthesis steers us to probe the literature in ways that were not possible in the past. One of the primary purposes of this volume is to illustrate some of the new directions in which research synthesis is heading.

Research synthesizers are seldom content simply to report average effect size. Rather, the conditions under which the effects occur or the subsets of persons who are most or least likely to be affected by intervention are usually of interest. In Chapter Four, Richard J. Light, one of the first to advocate research synthesis as a way of identifying important interactions, discusses several issues that synthesis alone can resolve. These resolutions are particularly applicable to policy decisions.

While research synthesis has expanded to new content areas and new user groups, the set of available statistical procedures has also expanded. In Chapter Two, Larry V. Hedges articulates some of the questions that contemporary statistical procedures can address. Hedges also discusses shortcomings of traditional analytic procedures for research synthesis in language that those not fluent in advanced statistics can understand. More important, he presents a mathematically correct alternative to traditional data synthesis analysis and uses examples to illustrate appropriate calculations.

The title of this sourcebook reflects the concern of its editors with methodological issues that are integral to research synthesis. Two of its chapters show how research synthesis can serve as a vehicle for the evaluation researcher who is methodologically inclined. In Chapter One, Bryant and Wortman demonstrate how the threats-to-validity approach developed by Donald Campbell and his colleagues can be used to guide both the choice of studies to include in the synthesis and the analyses that are performed. This approach is especially useful to evaluators who are interested in questions for which there are few high-quality studies, that is, true experiments. It also uses research synthesis in a self-scrutinizing way to assess the degree of distortion that is created when particular studies are excluded.

In Chapter Three, Yeaton and Wortman address many of the methodological issues raised by the study of new medical technologies. These authors discuss the importance of assessing the quantitative contribution of experimental design and offer a plausible explanation for this design effect. They present some tentative solutions for synthesizers whose interest is substantive fields in which considerable change occurs during the time period under study, and they point out the relevance of these solutions to mental health technologies.

Increasingly, decision makers are realizing the value of research synthesis in helping to shape public policy. In Chapter Five, Chelimsky and Morra show how the GAO's evaluation synthesis has been used to assist congressional policy deliberations. While most research syntheses have been targets of opportunity, the work of Chelimsky and Morra has had to be particularly creative, since relevant congressional problems have been dropped in their laps, and these problems have typically addressed matters of process, not of outcome. The fact that a well-done research synthesis can be conducted within the limited time frame created by congressional need has been of critical importance to their work.

As in the case of any technology that has been used for a number of years, people will ask what effect research synthesis has had on evaluation itself. In our opinion, not only have research synthesis procedures become an important supplement to the traditional literature review, with important uses that we have just outlined, but the synthesis strategy itself has the potential for changing the practice of primary researchers. Based on our own experiences, we concluded that the process of conducting a synthesis alters dramatically the way in which one looks at a field of study. Plans for new evaluative research studies are easily identified, and formative improvements in current evaluation procedures seem to appear almost automatically. In much the same way, the users of research syntheses, whether they agree with the approach or not, are provided with summaries highlighting measurement and design issues that force them to consider the weight that they place on different kinds of evidence. These are the very issues that evaluation researchers must confront in planning their studies. Certainly, failure to provide information pertinent to the user's conceptual framework may spur further study. Moreover, evidence that primary studies have been deficient in reporting relevant information

4

may shame journal editors and reviewers into becoming more meticulous about their own admission standards, since their publications may become part of someone else's research synthesis.

Ultimately, the real value of research synthesis may rest not on its use in reviewing empirical study of a given area but in its effects of primary research. Like any technology, its survival may be determined by its ability to evolve and compete successfully with formidable rivals. Taking this as our criterion, we conclude that research synthesis will play a substantial part in the systematic progress of our science.

William H. Yeaton
Paul M. Wortman
Editors

William H. Yeaton is assistant research scientist at the Center for Research on the Utilization of Scientific Knowledge at the University of Michigan. His current research interests include evaluation research methodology and medical technology assessment.

Paul M. Wortman is director of the Methodology and Evaluation Research Program in the Institute for Social Research and professor in the School of Public Health at the University of Michigan–Ann Arbor. His current research interests include research synthesis methods and medical technology assessment.

Special problems arise when meta-analysis is applied to
quasi-experiments. Careful consideration of threats to each
study's validity may help the meta-analyst to avoid these pitfalls.

Methodological Issues in the Meta-Analysis of Quasi-Experiments

Fred B. Bryant
Paul M. Wortman

Locate all available studies on a topic . . . eliminate from consideration
studies with severe methodological inadequacies. Results from
these studies are likely to be more misleading than helpful.
                                        Mansfield and Busse, 1977, p. 3

It's bad advice to eliminate virtually any studies on strictly
methodological grounds.
                                        Glass, 1978, p. 3

How should meta-analysts proceed when deciding which evidence to include in a synthesis of the research literature on a given subject or issue? The two epigraphs to this chapter represent diametrically opposed viewpoints on this

The authors thank Craig King for his assistance in the research synthesis of desegregation studies, Judy Savage for typing the manuscript, and Linda Perloff for helpful comments on an earlier version of this chapter. The research reported in this chapter was supported by grant NIE–G–79–0128 from the National Institute of Education.

W. H. Yeaton, P. M. Wortman (Eds.). *Issues in Data Synthesis.*
New Directions for Program Evaluation, no. 24. San Francisco: Jossey-Bass, December 1984.

5

issue. Should meta-analysts abandon critical judgments about the quality of primary research and include all available studies in data syntheses, or should they exclude flawed studies that suffer from threats to validity?

Such questions become especially important when the research literature of interest is largely quasi-experimental. In contrast to traditional literatures, in which most studies are randomized true experiments, much evaluation research involves nonrandomized quasi-experiments, which have methodological weaknesses (Cook and Campbell, 1979; Rossi and Williams, 1972). Indeed, in some cases the evidence that they provide can hardly be considered valid. Thus, quasi-experiments represent a particularly problematic area for the debate about selectivity in the choice of evidence for research synthesis.

In this chapter, we argue that meta-analysts need to address two issues when considering studies for inclusion: the range of experimental rigor within the particular research literature and their own priorities regarding internal and external validity. In some content areas, there may be enough randomized true experiments with which those of poorer quality can be compared (Wortman and Yeaton, 1983). In these cases, the meta-analyst may be justified in including all studies, regardless of their methodological quality. However, in content areas where all studies are nonrandomized quasi-experiments, there may be no high-quality baseline with which poorer-quality studies can be compared. In these cases, if enough studies are available, the meta-analyst can exclude studies with severe methodological flaws and include only studies of relatively high quality. Further, the unavoidable trade-offs between methodological rigor and representativeness force investigators who favor external validity to be more inclusive in choosing evidence and investigators who favor internal validity to be more selective.

In this chapter, we examine two sets of decisions, one regarding relevance, the other regarding acceptability, that meta-analysts must make when evaluating evidence for inclusion in research syntheses. For each set of decisions, we analyze the issues raised by the validity of primary studies. We illustrate our analysis with examples drawn from a recent research synthesis of quasi-experiments on school desegregation and black student achievement (Wortman and Bryant, forthcoming). Next, we consider the consequences of decisions to exclude studies in the context of our synthesis of desegregation research. We then explore how different criteria for the selection and analysis of evidence can yield different meta-analytic conclusions. Last, we discuss ways of resolving the inevitable disagreements that will arise among meta-analysts.

Criteria for Evaluation of Research Studies

Two different sets of decisions must be made when evaluating research evidence for inclusion in research syntheses. First, we must decide whether a given study is relevant to the questions of interest in the research synthesis. Second, we must decide which of the studies deemed relevant should be included in the research synthesis. One way of understanding these two sets of decisions is to consider them in terms of Cook and Campbell's (1979) four types of validity: construct validity, external validity, statistical conclusion validity, and internal validity. As Wortman (1983) notes, the first set of decisions is largely an issue of construct and external validity, whereas the second set of decisions focuses primarily on statistical conclusion and internal validity. The following section describes this selection procedure.

Decisions Regarding Relevance

Construct Validity. Construct validity concerns the degree to which the treatments and outcome measures of a particular study accurately represent the relevant underlying constructs (Cook and Campbell, 1979). We can judge a study to be irrelevant on grounds of low construct validity if its independent or dependent variables involve constructs that differ from those specified in the meta-analytic research question. Thus, in our synthesis of the desegregation literature (Wortman and Bryant, forthcoming), we formulated the following research question: What are the effects of U.S. public school desegregation on the achievement (that is, general, reading, or mathematics test scores) of black students bused to previously all-white schools? To compute effect size, we decided to use the traditional meta-analysis formula (Cohen, 1977; Glass, 1976) whereby the posttest mean of the segregated group was subtracted from the posttest mean of the desegregated group and the resulting difference was divided by the posttest standard deviation of the segregated group.

On close reading, some of the studies that investigated treatments labeled *desegregation* or outcomes labeled *achievement* operationalized these constructs in invalid ways. With respect to the construct validity of treatment, we decided to ignore studies in which interventions did not involve racial desegregation, such as studies of bus transportation per se (for example, Davies, 1969). We also rejected studies that compared untreated control groups of all-black classrooms with "desegregated" classrooms in which most students were actually black (for example, Akin, 1977), since such treatments did not represent racial desegregation (Armor, 1972).

With respect to the construct validity of outcome measures, we decided to ignore studies in which outcomes were not measured by standardized tests of math, reading, or general achievement. Thus, we excluded studies using IQ scores (for example, Moorehead, 1972), grade point averages (for example, Hayden, 1976), dropout rates (for example, Felice and Richardson, 1976), and unstandardized tests (for example, Geiger, 1968). We also rejected studies that aggregated achievement test scores across all participating ethnic minorities (for example, Purl and Dawson, 1973), since ethnically heterogenous scores did not specifically measure black students' achievement.

Judgments regarding the relevance of a given study's constructs are fundamental when choosing evidence for inclusion in research syntheses. All meta-analysts use construct validity criteria to some extent in selecting their data base. If we are overly inclusive, we run the risk of compiling a hodge-podge of information from which meaningful conclusions cannot be drawn (Gallo, 1978). Indeed, as Cook and Leviton (1980) have noted, it would be poor practice not to exclude studies that are irrelevant on theoretical grounds.

However, our restrictiveness in judging the relevance of study constructs depends on the specificity of our research question (Wortman, 1983). If we have formulated a highly detailed research question that specifies a precise set of critical constructs, then we will have to be fairly restrictive in selecting relevant studies. In contrast, if our research question is relatively general and if it encompasses a relatively wide range of constructs, then we can be relatively permissive in selecting relevant studies. Thus, meta-analysts with narrow research questions typically draw conclusions of fairly limited representativeness (Cooper, 1982).

External Validity. External validity concerns the degree to which the settings, populations, or time periods involved in a particular study restrict the generalizability of its results (Campbell and Stanley, 1966; Cook and Campbell, 1979). We can judge a given study to be irrelevant on grounds of low external validity if its setting, research population, or historical period diverges from those specified in the meta-analytic research question. Thus, because of the specific nature of our research question, we decided to ignore studies that occurred in settings other than U.S. public schools, such as private schools (for example, Gardner and others, 1970), kindergartens (for example, Dawson, 1973), or schools outside the United States (for example, Dunlop and others, 1958). We also decided to ignore studies that involved only desegregated populations other than blacks, such as white students (for example, Cypert, 1971) and Hispanic children (for example, Mahard and Crain, 1980). In addition, we excluded studies that occurred before the 1954 Supreme Court decision (for example, Crowley, 1932) that made desegregation a public policy issue.

Another limitation to the generalizability of a study's results is created by failure to report when and where the experimental treatment occurred. Thus, we excluded studies that did not report the dates or locations of desegregation interventions (for example, Morrison, 1972), because such omissions prevented us from making judgments about their relevance to our specific research question.

Another strategy for handling cases of insufficient reporting is to contact the original researcher and request the missing information (Cordray and Orwin, 1983). However, this approach goes beyond meta-analysis of primary research toward a form of secondary analysis, and in practice it may be relatively inefficient. For example, in a meta-analysis of research on cognitive gender differences, Hyde (1981) wrote letters requesting unreported statistics to the authors of eighteen different studies. She received seven responses, and only two provided the information that she had requested. Bias may also be operating, such that those who respond may be systematically different from those who do not. While it may be easier for primary researchers to provide information about dates and locations than it is to furnish unreported statistics, rates of response to requests for additional information of any kind are notoriously low. Bryant and Wortman (1978) analyze this problem in some detail.

If the meta-analyst decides to contact primary investigators to obtain missing information, he or she must avoid being selective in choosing which studies to pursue, because the researcher's own prejudices can bias the process of requesting unreported information. In order not to introduce such bias, the meta-analyst who decides to pursue incomplete reports should request information for all studies that lack necessary details, not just for those whose findings support the meta-analyst's hypothesis or political viewpoint. In our research synthesis of desegregation studies (Wortman and Bryant, forthcoming) the funding agency — the National Institute of Education — convened a panel of experts with contrasting attitudes on busing to evaluate our methods and findings. Several panel members suggested that we request missing information from primary researchers. Interestingly, some opponents of busing suggested contacting only authors whose findings were negative. In fact, the panel only contacted the author of one study, whose findings were negative, to obtain missing information.

As with judgments of relevance concerning construct validity, the degree to which meta-analysts must consider the relevance of a study's settings, populations, and dates of conduct varies with the specificity of their research question (Bryant, 1983). Meta-analysts who formulate highly detailed research questions that specify precise treatment locales, target populations, or chronological periods must be relatively restrictive in selecting relevant studies. Meta-analysts who formulate relatively general research questions can be more inclusive in selecting relevant evidence. As a result, investigators with narrower research questions will exclude as irrelevant many studies that investigators with broader research questions will include. Again, selectivity limits the generalizablity of conclusions drawn from research syntheses (Cooper, 1982). Although the formulation of the research question itself is in principle the major determinant in selecting the evidence for meta-analysis, such other factors as cost, convenience, and comparability of dependent variables can make the selection process somewhat more interactive.

Decisions Regarding Acceptability

After selecting relevant studies for research synthesis, we may decide that some studies seem more appropriate for inclusion than others. While it can be relatively easy to justify the exclusion of studies that we deem to be irrelevant to our research question, disagreements can arise if we wish to reject some relevant studies as unacceptable for research synthesis. In this section, we will examine such decisions about acceptability in light of the statistical conclusion validity and internal validity described by Cook and Campbell (1979).

Statistical Conclusion Validity. Statistical conclusion validity concerns the degree to which valid inferences can be drawn from the statistical analyses performed in a particular study (Cook and Campbell, 1979). We may judge a given study to be unacceptable on grounds of low statistical conclusion validity if it lacks the necessary descriptive statistics for evaluation and coding, or if it involves only statistical comparisons other than those specified in the meta-analytic research question. Thus, in our synthesis of desegregation research, we decided to exclude summary statements that lacked statistical information (for example, Beers and Reardon, 1974) as well as nonempirical literature reviews (for example, Weinberg, 1977). Moreover, some of the relevant empirical studies provided us with insufficient information to derive necessary means, standard deviations, or sample sizes for meta-analysis (for example, Calhoun, 1978). As with nonempirical reports that lacked data, these studies, too, had to be excluded from our meta-analysis. As an alternative, we could have contacted the authors of these studies to request unreported statistics. However, since this strategy goes beyond the normal role of meta-analysis and since it is not likely to be successful, we chose not to do so.

Other relevant studies provided sufficient information, but they suffered from flaws that invalidated their statistical comparisons, such as very inadequate sample sizes (for example, Teele, 1973) and inappropriate use of statistical tests (for example, Phillips and Bianchi, 1975) where the raw data are unavailable. Because inferential statistics are misleading in such cases (Cook and Campbell, 1979), we decided to reject these studies. Mansfield and Busse (1977) also have argued that studies involving very small sample sizes should be eliminated to avoid capitalizing on chance (Gilbert and others, 1977).

Another threat to statistical conclusion validity that we considered when judging relevant studies for acceptability involved random heterogeneity in the sample of respondents (Cook and Campbell, 1979). For instance, several relevant desegregation studies globally combined data across different grade levels to test for treatment effects (for example, Lemke, 1979). Because this approach allows variations in the age of students and in the duration of the treatment to influence statistical conclusions, we decided to reject these studies. We also ignored desegregation studies that reported only statistical comparisons across ethnicity; that is, we rejected studies that compared black students' test scores with white students' test scores (for example, Merchant, 1969), because we considered such comparisons to be statistically invalid assessments of black students' achievement. Including them could have threatened the construct validity of the meta-analytic statistic.

As with judgments about the relevance of a given study's constructs, judgments regarding the acceptability of a given study's statistical comparisons are unavoidable when choosing studies for meta-analysis. Studies that provide no statistical information and studies that make irrelevant comparisons must necessarily be discarded. For example, nonempirical investigations provide no outcome data, and thus they are unacceptable as evidence in meta-analysis. Studies involving only inappropriate comparisons must also be rejected in order to preserve the validity of meta-analytic conclusions.

In contrast to judgments of relevance concerning construct and external validity, however, judgments regarding the acceptability of a study's statistical comparisons are relatively independent of the specificity of the research question. Whether the research question is specific or general, certain rules of valid statistical inference must be maintained when selecting appropriate evidence. Clearly, the absence of appropriate statistical information or of tables containing raw data necessitates exclusion, no matter what the research question is. Similarly, although decisions to reject particular statistical comparisons can be more clear-cut when the research question is very specific, some types of comparisons are always irrelevant. Because judgments of acceptability based on statistical conclusion validity are required to some extent in order to assure valid results, they represent a necessary restriction in the representativeness of meta-analytic conclusions. In some cases, the lack of appropriate statistical information can be overcome by contacting the original authors (Wortman and Bryant, forthcoming). The limitations of this procedure have already been noted.

Internal Validity. Internal validity concerns the degree to which valid causal inferences can be drawn from the methodology used in a particular study (Campbell and Stanley, 1966; Cook and Campbell, 1979). By far the most controversial decisions regarding the acceptability of relevant studies concern studies whose methodology prevents valid causal inferences (Wortman, 1983). On the one hand, Glass (1976, 1977, 1978) and his colleagues (Glass and others, 1981; Glass and Smith, 1978) have repeatedly argued that meta-analysts should not exclude studies on the basis of methodological quality. They maintain that all available studies on a topic should be included and that the effects of design quality should be examined a posteriori. On the other hand, critics of meta-analysis (Eysenck, 1978; Mansfield and Busse, 1977) have argued that studies with methodological weaknesses should be discarded in favor of studies with high design quality. These authors maintain that the conclusions that we can draw from a research synthesis are only as valid as the evidence on which it is based (Eysenck, 1978).

Proponents of the traditional all-inclusive approach argue that the influence of design quality on treatment effects is essentially an empirical issue that is best examined by combining all available studies across the full range of methodological rigor (Glass, 1978; Glass and Smith, 1978), and they recommend including all studies even when most are methodologically weak (Glass, 1977). This viewpoint assumes a type of strategic combination argument (Staines, 1974)—that flawed studies can be combined because their weaknesses when pooled will cancel out each other and yield a coherent, unbiased result (Wortman and Bryant, forthcoming). However, when all studies share a common bias, this all-inclusive approach can be misleading. Research synthesis may not be able to detect bias that operates predominantly in one direction (Cook and Leviton, 1980; Wortman, 1983), and if it does detect bias, it may not be able to correct it. Without well-designed studies that can be used as a baseline for comparison, it is impossible to determine how methodological quality affects results (Jackson, 1980). Thus, rather than canceling each other out, shared sources of bias can simply create one large, biased set of evidence.

The research literature on school desegregation exemplifies this problem. Research on desegregation is almost exclusively quasi-experimental, and its methodology is extremely uneven in quality. Indeed, desegregation studies generally share the same major sources of bias. For example, treatment and control groups are usually self-selected, so that desegregated students typically begin with higher initial achievement test scores (Wortman and Bryant, forthcoming). In the absence of well-designed studies that can be used as a standard of comparison, it is difficult to use traditional meta-analytic procedures to adjust effect size for this selection bias. In the few cases for which pretest data are available, it may be possible to remove much of the selection bias from the posttest results with nontraditional techniques (Wortman and Bryant, forthcoming).

For this reason, we decided to reject relevant desegregation studies that suffered from threats to their internal validity and to consider only a relatively pure subset of studies for research synthesis. For example, we excluded cross sectional surveys of students in schools distributed across a wide geographical area (for example, McPartland, 1969). Because these nonexperimental research designs rarely permit control of factors that can influence academic achievement independently of school desegregation, we believe that they are inherently weak and that they have little use for program evaluation and policy development.

We also rejected studies that lacked adequate nondesegregated control group data. In these cases, comparison groups consisted of district or statewide test norms (for example, Purl and Dawson, 1973), cohort data from a different historical period (for example, Prichard, 1969), or "segregated" students who had in fact experienced some form of desegregation (for example, Sacramento City Unified School District, 1971). Such comparisons constitute invalid tests of desegregation in which inadequate experimental controls are likely to produce artifactual achievement differences. We also excluded studies that used different achievement tests for segregated and desegregated students (for example, Danahy, 1971). These studies suffer from instrumentation threats (Campbell and Stanley, 1966; Cook and Campbell, 1979) of differential test reliability that can either produce spurious treatment effects or mask true effects.

In constrast to the literature on school desegregation, research literatures that contain a relatively large portion of high-quality evidence can afford the meta-analyst the luxury of integrating the full range of available studies. Traditional experimental literatures usually contain at least some studies of high methodological quality with which poorer-quality studies can be compared (Wortman and Yeaton, 1983). The all-inclusive approach can be justified in these cases, since the meta-analyst possesses an absolute, high-quality baseline against which the effects of bias can be assessed.

The preceding discussion suggests that it would be shortsighted to recommend either the all-inclusive or the methodologically selective approach for all research syntheses. Whether the meta-analyst should be inclusive or selective depends on the range of experimental rigor in the particular research literature. Content areas that contain well-designed true experiments may offer a sufficient number of high-quality studies with which the studies of poorer quality can be compared. In contrast, in content areas that contain only quasi-experiments there may not be enough studies of high methodological quality to afford the meta-analyst a standard of comparison. Thus, he or she may be forced to exclude the studies with severe flaws in order to obtain a set of higher-quality evidence for research synthesis.

Effects of Decisions to Exclude Studies

Final Samples

As already noted, we decided to exclude studies from our synthesis of the desegregation literature (Wortman and Bryant, forthcoming) that were irrelevant to our research question. Of the 157 studies retrieved, close reading revealed that 46 (29 percent) were irrelevant because of inappropriate constructs, settings, populations, historical periods, statistical comparisons, or research designs. After eliminating these studies, we were left with a total of 111 studies (71 percent) that appropriately addressed issues of interest to our research synthesis. From the relevant studies, we eliminated those that were unacceptably flawed. Of the 111 studies deemed relevant, 80 (72 percent) were judged to be unacceptable for research synthesis because of excessive threats to their statistical conclusion or internal validity. This left a sample of thirty-one methodologically pure studies for our analyses. Thus, we judged that only 20 percent of the studies that we retrieved and 28 percent of the studies that we deemed relevant were acceptable for research synthesis.

Comparing Acceptable and Unacceptable Studies

When validity criteria are used to exclude some portion of relevant studies, a question naturally arises as to the comparability of acceptable and unacceptable studies. Do the acceptable and unacceptable differ systematically in some other respects besides methodological quality? Is a form of confirmatory bias (Lord and others, 1979; Mahoney, 1977) operating so that the studies that are accepted tend more to confirm the investigator's expectations and beliefs than the rejected studies do? Regardless of their nature, any differences between accepted and rejected studies represent limits on the generalizability of research conclusions that meta-analysts should identify and acknowledge (Cooper, 1982). Table 1 summarizes some of the differences between the studies that we accepted and rejected for our research synthesis.

Characteristics of the Desegregation Intervention. Desegregation interventions in the accepted studies were more likely to be voluntary or de facto plans in New England or Middle Atlantic states that involved cross-district busing of black students from urban schools to other urban or to suburban schools. Desegregation interventions in rejected studies were more likely to be mandatory plans in South Atlantic states that involved intradistrict busing of black students from suburban schools to other suburban schools. Accepted studies used fewer sending and receiving schools, had smaller percentages of blacks in desegregated groups, and had larger differences in the percentage of blacks between segregated and desegregated groups than rejected studies did.

**Table 1. Summary of Selected Chi Square Analyses
Comparing Accepted and Rejected Studies**

Variable	Accepted Studies	Rejected Studies
Type of Desegregation Plan [a]		
Mandatory ($N = 88$)	9.6%	43.1%
Voluntary ($N = 157$)	71.2%	45.9%
De facto ($N = 40$)	19.2%	11.0%
Types of Sending and Receiving Schools [b]		
Urban–urban ($N = 187$)	74.7%	62.0%
Urban–suburban ($N = 38$)	22.0%	9.4%
Rural–rural ($N = 6$)	0.0%	3.1%
Suburban–suburban ($N = 18$)	3.3%	25.5%
Geographical Location of Study [a,c]		
New England ($N = 26$)	14.2%	5.2%
Middle Atlantic ($N = 45$)	27.4%	7.5%
East North Central ($N = 87$)	22.6%	29.6%
West North Central ($N = 7$)	0.0%	3.3%
South Atlantic ($N = 54$)	6.6%	22.1%
East South Central ($N = 8$)	1.9%	2.8%
West South Central ($N = 45$)	15.0%	13.6%
Mountain ($N = 7$)	1.9%	2.3%
Pacific ($N = 40$)	10.4%	13.6%
Type of Research Design [a]		
One-group pretest-posttest ($N = 71$)	17.0%	28.5%
Pretest-posttest nonequivalent control group ($N = 144$)	57.5%	44.6%

Table 1. Summary of Selected Chi Square Analyses
Comparing Accepted and Rejected Studies (cont'd.)

Variable	Accepted Studies	Rejected Studies
Type of Research Design [a] (continued)		
Static group comparison ($N = 70$)	18.9%	26.9%
Randomized study ($N = 7$)	6.6%	0.0%
Method of Forming Control Group [a]		
Random sampling ($N = 50$)	26.0%	13.1%
Matching ($N = 51$)	30.0%	11.5%
National norms ($N = 19$)	0.0%	10.4%
Historical data ($N = 37$)	0.0%	20.2%
Predicted score ($N = 11$)	0.0%	6.0%
Subjects as own control ($N = 71$)	14.0%	31.1%
Full universe ($N = 44$)	30.0%	7.7%
Type of Publication [a]		
Technical report ($N = 161$)	41.5%	51.1%
Article or book ($N = 53$)	3.8%	21.4%
Dissertation or thesis ($N = 121$)	54.7%	27.5%
Type of Outcome [d]		
Reading Achievement		
Positive effect ($N = 86$)	34.6%	42.5%
Zero effect ($N = 85$)	51.9%	36.2%
Negative effect ($N = 41$)	13.5%	21.3%
Math Achievement		
Positive effect ($N = 69$)	48.6%	40.0%
Zero effect ($N = 62$)	42.8%	36.2%
Negative effect ($N = 34$)	8.6%	23.8%
General Achievement [b]		
Positive effect ($N = 25$)	37.5%	40.7%
Zero effect ($N - 18$)	62.5%	24.1%
Negative effect ($N = 19$)	0.0%	35.2%

Note: The analyses summarized here used cases—separate comparisons of a treatment and a control group—within each study as the unit of analysis. On the average, there were 3.05 cases per study, with accepted studies providing 3.42 cases and rejected studies providing 2.90 cases. Using the study as the unit of analysis did not change the interpretation of these results.

[a] $p < .01$
[b] $p < .05$
[c] This coding scheme is based on the U.S. Census Bureau categorization of states into regions.
[d] This vote-counting (Light and Smith, 1971) categorization of overall results is based on the conclusions drawn by the authors of the studies subjected to meta-analysis. We also attempted to categorize each study's outcomes according to our own judgment of the conclusions that were justified. However, this strategy led us to code the vast majority of reading, mathematics, and general achievement outcomes as not ascertainable because of the threats to validity. For this reason, we have only reported the results of comparisons using the authors' conclusions.

Characteristics of the Study. Accepted studies were more likely to involve pretest-posttest nonequivalent control group designs and smaller comparison groups. Rejected studies were more likely to involve one-group pretest-posttest designs and larger control groups formed by using black students before desegregation, national norms, or historical data. Compared with the two-group designs, the weaker one-group quasi-experiments were generally confounded by such threats to internal validity as selection, maturation, and mortality (Campbell and Stanley, 1966; Cook and Campbell, 1979), which are associated with inflated estimates of effect size in desegregation research (Wortman and Bryant, forthcoming).

In addition, we were more likely to accept dissertations and theses and to reject articles and books. Studies published in professional journals or books often lacked the information necessary to extract an effect size or to make judgments about construct, external, statistical conclusion, or internal validity. In contrast, the typical dissertation or thesis contained highly detailed information specifying operations, methods, sampling procedures, and statistical comparisons. Consequently, we were more likely to find a level of detail sufficient for coding among dissertations and theses than among articles and books. We also found that studies published in journals and books had larger effect sizes than unpublished studies did. This publication bias has been noted by other meta-analysts (for example, Smith, 1980) across a variety of content areas. This suggests that retrieval techniques that rely only on published reports may overestimate effect size (Bryant, 1983; Cooper, 1982).

Historical Differences. On the average, accepted studies were conducted at an earlier point in history than the rejected studies were. The year of the pretest and posttest, the year in which the desegregation intervention began, and the date on which the report was made public were earlier for accepted studies than they were for rejected studies. On the average, the rejected studies were conducted in the late 1960s, and the accepted studies were conducted earlier in the 1960s.

These historical differences between accepted and rejected studies help to explain the differences in desegregation interventions and study characteristics just noted. School districts in New England or Middle Atlantic states tended to implement desegregation plans of their own volition early in the 1960s. These voluntary interventions typically involved fewer sending and receiving schools and the percentages of blacks in the desegregated groups were typically smaller. Because voluntary plans could be implemented in some segregated schools and not in others, separate control groups of nonbused black students could be formed from all-black schools. In these cases, the strong comparison group or nonequivalent control group design (Campbell and Stanley, 1966) could be used to evaluate the intervention. Since this design suffers from fewer threats to internal validity than others do, we were more likely to include studies that used it in our research synthesis.

In contrast, it was not until the late 1960s that school districts in the

South were ordered by courts to implement mandatory desegregation plans. These forced-busing interventions typically involved more sending and receiving schools, and the percentages of blacks in the desegregated groups were typically larger. Because the court-ordered plans generally required desegregating every all-black classroom in the school district, groups of non-bused black students rarely remained to serve as separate control groups. In these cases, one-group pretest-posttest designs or historical controls were the only methodological recourse available. And, as mentioned earlier, these weak designs suffer from substantial threats to internal validity, which made us more likely to exclude the studies that used them from our research synthesis. Differences in the characteristics of accepted and rejected studies thus appear to be logical offshoots of the historical development of school desegregation.

Differences in Outcomes. Another crucial question raised in comparing the accepted and rejected studies is this: Did the two sets of studies find different effects? Although we ignored study results when judging threats to validity, the critical observer may still wonder whether we unintentionally produced systematic differences between study outcomes when selecting among studies for high-quality evidence. Unfortunately, many of the studies that we rejected failed to provide necessary statistical information, so we could not directly compare effect sizes for the two sets of studies. However, we were able to use a rough vote-counting method (Light and Smith, 1971) to categorize the direction of reported effects and to compare frequencies of outcomes for accepted and rejected studies. The "type of outcome" section in Table 1 presents the results of these vote-counting analyses for each type of achievement test.

Although math and reading achievement tests showed no significant differences, accepted studies were more likely to find no effects, and rejected studies were more likely to find negative effects, for general achievement tests. This finding indicates that slight systematic biases in general achievement outcomes may exist between the two sets of studies. Obviously, this crude ordinal categorization is not precise enough to allow us to distinguish differences in the magnitude of effects.

Experimental Rigor Versus Representativeness

It is clear from these comparative analyses that the final sample of studies included in our research synthesis was not representative of the entire body of evidence. In selecting only evidence of relatively high methodological quality, we compiled a set of studies that differed systematically from the set of studies that we rejected. Thus, we made a conscious choice between two sets of priorities — maximizing the validity of causal inferences and maximizing the generalizability of research conclusions. We chose to place more weight on internal validity than on external validity.

Because these two sets of priorities tend to be mutually exclusive (Cook and Campbell, 1979), researchers must usually sacrifice one objective in gaining the other. That is, they must typically make a trade-off between unequivocal results whose generalizability is limited and equivocal results that are widely generalizable. Consequently, the reseacher's scientific priorities largely determine the researcher's decision to be more selective or more inclusive in choosing evidence for research synthesis. Researchers who consider external validity to be more important (Cronbach and others, 1980) will favor the all-inclusive approach. Researchers who consider internal validity to be more important (Campbell and Stanley, 1966) will favor the methodologically selective approach. We opted to be more selective, because we believe that internal validity is a sine qua non in experimentation.

Yet, even when external validity takes priority in research synthesis, the specific types of generalizations that the researcher wishes to make will influence his or her selectivity when choosing evidence. Those who wish to generalize across a variety of settings, populations, or historical periods will be more inclusive. Those who wish to generalize to specific settings, populations, or historical periods will be more selective (Cook and Campbell, 1979). Thus, the range of evidence that the researcher selects depends not only on his or her scientific priorities but also on the purposes of the research synthesis.

The Limits of Selectivity

But, just how far should selectivity go? We excluded 80 percent of the studies that we retrieved for our research synthesis, so that our final sample contained thirty-one studies. It is easy to imagine instances in which the selective meta-analyst is left with even fewer acceptable studies (Berk and Chalmers, 1981). As restrictions on the number of studies selected for inclusion increase, research synthesis at some point ceases to be a quantitative integration of an entire body of evidence as in meta-analysis, and becomes just a rigorous, systematic literature review.

What is the minimum number of studies that a research synthesis should include? This question may best be addressed by considering meta-analysis as analogous to primary research (Saxe, 1983). Primary researchers impose entry criteria for the admission of subjects into studies and data analyses. In much the same way, we have argued, meta-analysts must use criteria for admitting studies into research syntheses. To select relevant evidence, studies should be evaluated for their contruct and external validity. To select acceptable evidence, studies should be evaluated for their statistical conclusion and internal validity. To extend the analogy, just as the primary researcher must determine the minimum number of subjects to include in primary research, so must the meta-analyst determine the number of studies to include in research synthesis. In making such decisions, primary researchers use statistical power analysis (Cohen, 1977) to specify minimum sample size as a function of the effect size under investigation. Required sample size increases as effect size decreases. Analogously, meta-analysts can use power curves (Feldt and Mahmoud, 1958) to determine the minimum number of studies or outcomes that must be included, given the expected magnitude of effects. Research literatures in which effects are relatively small will thus require a relatively large minimum number of studies, while literatures in which effects are relatively large will require a relatively small minimum number of studies.

The Inevitability of Disagreement

Although individual meta-analysts may use the same criteria to select evidence for research synthesis, they may make different subjective judgments that in turn yield different meta-analytic conclusions (Bryant, 1983). For example, the panel of experts convened by NIE to review our work on studies of school desegregation essentially agreed with the set of threats to validity that we used in selecting evidence. However, in performing their own independent research syntheses, individual panel members tended to obtain slightly different estimates of the average effect size. These estimates ranged from about + .04 to + .30. Although panel members agreed that desegregation had no negative effects on black student achievement, they disagreed on the size of the positive effects; opponents of busing found the smallest positive effects, while proponents of busing found the largest effects.

These disagreements about average effect size can be traced to three different types of decisions that meta-analysts must make. First, disagreements can arise from decisions about the studies to include in research synthesis. Different sets of primary studies can yield different meta-analytic results (Bryant, 1983; Cooper, 1982).

Second, disagreements can arise from decisions about the comparisons to consider within a given study. Choices about which comparison group or which comparison between treatment and control groups to use can cause estimates of effect size to vary. Indeed, NIE panel members often selected only those comparisons within a particular study that supported their own ideological viewpoint.

Third, disagreements can arise from decisions about the type of data analysis to perform. Different analysis strategies can yield different meta-analytic results. For example, one NIE panel member decided to adjust effect sizes for differences in the ages of the children involved, whereas others computed a traditional estimate of effect size (Cohen, 1977; Glass, 1976). However, a number of alternatives are available. We could reduce bias in our estimates of effect size by using the pooled within-group standard deviation as a denominator (Hedges, 1981), by weighting for sample size (Hedges, 1982), or by adjusting for unreliability in measures (Hunter and others, 1982); we could correct posttest effect sizes for any pretest differences between treatment and control groups (Wortman and Bryant, forthcoming); we could use significance levels from the primary studies to quantify treatment effects (Rosenthal, 1980); or we could use vote-counting methods to categorize results (Light and Smith, 1971). Each technique could yield different results.

Because research synthesis will always entail subjective judgments on the part of the meta-analyst, disagreements among individual meta-analysts are unavoidable. We thus return full circle to the point from which we began: First, we confronted inconsistencies in the findings of primary studies. Then, we considered meta-analysis as a means of resolving these inconsistencies. Now, we find that research syntheses themselves can reach different findings.

Recommendations

How should we respond to the inevitability of disagreement? Perhaps the best way of addressing this issue is to consider the analogy between meta-analysis and primary research. To help resolve contradictions among primary researchers, Campbell (1971, 1979) has suggested that investigators should make their data publicly available for secondary analysis by others. This practice would allow independent researchers with different theoretical and methodological perspectives to examine the same set of evidence, as the NIE panel did for our study. If their results converge, then our confidence in the overall conclusions increases. For the NIE panel, for example, the results form a kind of confidence interval that "brackets" (Wortman and others, 1978) a positive effect. If their results diverge, then we can pinpoint sources of disagreement by comparing different researchers' decisions about the cases to include, the statistical comparisons to make, and the types of analyses to perform. However, such pinpointing is possible only if both primary and meta-analytic data are publicly available.

Perhaps applying Campbell's notions about primary research to research synthesis would help to resolve the inevitable disagreements among meta-analysts. If meta-analytic data bases are archived and made publicly available, then investigators with different perspectives can synthesize exactly the same sets of evidence. If they were to do so, we could identify sources of disagreement among meta-analysts and explore the consequences of decisions about which studies to include, which comparisons within studies to consider, and which types of analyses to perform. For example, Smith and Glass's (1977) meta-analysis of psychotherapy outcome studies has been reanalyzed by Landman and Dawes (1982), who adjusted effect sizes for nonindependence and replicated the original findings on a random subset of the original studies. Even more recently, Orwin and Cordray (1983) resynthesized the same literature, selecting a stratified random sample of studies from Smith and Glass's bibliography and correcting for unreliability. This most recent reanalysis, however, obtained different results. Because the literature in question is widely accessible, all three meta-analyses were able to use a comparable data base. And because each investigation made public its criterion for selecting studies and for selecting comparisons within studies, all three meta-analyses used similar comparisons between experimental and control groups. Thus, we can conclude that differences in the type of analysis performed account for the discrepant conclusions.

The public availability of meta-analytic data sets will be especially critical for research literatures that contain a high proportion of inaccessible fugitive studies, as is the case for research on school desegregation. These data bases must include copies of the original research reports and codebooks. They should also identify the studies that were excluded as well as the criteria used in accepting and rejecting studies. By making our desegregation data base available to other investigators, we hope to promote meta-synthesis — that is, the cumulation and comparison of conclusions drawn from independent meta-analyses of the same research literature. Only by comparing results across different research syntheses that use different criteria to select and evaluate evidence can we ultimately converge on the underlying truth.

References

Akin, J. P. "A Study of the Relationship of Racial Integration to Reading Achievement in Grades 2, 3, and 5 in Alexandria, Virginia, City Public Schools." Unpublished doctoral dissertation, George Washington University, 1977. (ED 159 265)

Armor, D. J. "The Evidence on Busing." *The Public Interest,* 1972, *28,* 90–126.

Beers, J. S., and Reardon, F. J. "Racial Balancing in Harrisburg: Achievement and Attitudinal Changes." *Integrated Education,* 1974, *12* (5), 35–38.

Berk, A. A., and Chalmers, T. C. "Cost and Efficacy of the Substitution of Ambulatory for Inpatient Care." *New England Journal of Medicine,* 1981, *304* (7), 393–397.

Bryant, F. B. "Issues in Omitting Studies from Research Syntheses." Paper presented in the 1983 Joint Meeting of the Evaluation Research Society and Evaluation Network, Chicago, October 1983.

Bryant, F. B., and Wortman, P. M. "Secondary Analysis: The Case for Data Archives." *American Psychologist,* 1978, *33,* 381–387.

Calhoun, P. C. "A Study of the Effects of the Forced Desegregation Pairing of a Low-Socioeconomic-Status White Elementary School on Achievement, Social Interaction, and Enrollment." Unpublished doctoral dissertation, Georgia State University, 1978.

Campbell, D. T. "Reforms as Experiments." *Urban Affairs Quarterly,* 1971, *7,* 133–171.

Campbell, D. T. "Degrees of Freedom and the Case Study." In T. D. Cook and C. S. Reichardt (Eds.), *Qualitative and Quantitative Methods in Evaluation Research.* Beverly Hills, Calif.: Sage, 1979.

Campbell, D. T., and Stanley, J. C. *Experimental and Quasi-Experimental Designs for Research.* Chicago: Rand McNally, 1966.

Cohen, J. *Statistical Power Analysis for the Behavioral Sciences.* (Rev. ed.) New York: Academic Press, 1977.

Cook, T. D., and Campbell, D. T. *Quasi-Experimentation: Design and Analysis Issues for Field Settings.* Chicago: Rand McNally, 1979.

Cook, T. D., and Leviton, L. C. "Reviewing the Literature: A Comparison of Traditional Methods with Meta-Analysis." *Journal of Personality,* 1980, *48* (4), 449–472.

Cooper, H. M. "Scientific Guidelines for Conducting Integrative Research Reviews." *Review of Educational Research,* 1982, *52* (2), 291–302.

Cordray, D. S., and Orwin, R. G. "Improving the Quality of Evidence: Interconnections Among Primary Evaluation, Secondary Analysis, and Quantitative Synthesis." In R. J. Light (Ed.), *Evaluation Studies Review Annual*. Vol. 8. Beverly Hills, Calif.: Sage, 1983.

Cronbach, L. J., Ambron, S. R., Dornbusch, S. M., Hess, R. D., Hornik, R. C., Phillips, D. C., Walker, D. F., and Weiner, S. S. *Toward Reform of Program Evaluation: Aims, Methods, and Institutional Arrangements*. San Francisco: Jossey-Bass, 1980.

Crowley, M. R. "Cincinnati's Experiment in Negro Education: A Comparative Study of the Segregated and Mixed School." *Journal of Negro Education*, 1932, *1*, 25–33.

Cypert, K. E. "The Immediate Effects of Classroom Integration on the Academic Progress, Self-Concept, and Racial Attitudes of Elementary White Students." Unpublished doctoral dissertation, North Texas State University, 1971.

Danahy, A. H. "A Study of the Effects of Busing on the Achievement, Attendance, Attitudes, and Social Choices of Negro Inner-City Children." Unpublished doctoral dissertation, University of Minnesota, 1971.

Davies, E. A., Jr. "A Comparative Study of the Academic Achievement of Transported and Nontransported Pupils at Holly Hill Elementary School, Holly Hill, Florida." Unpublished master's thesis, Stetson University, 1969.

Lawson, J. A. *A Longitudinal Cross Sectional Study of Achievement of Black and Spanish-Surnamed Students in Desegregated Elementary and Secondary Schools*. Riverside Unified School District, 1973. (ED 086 770)

Dunlop, G. M., Harper, R. J. C., and Hunka, S. "The Influence of Transporting Children to Centralized Schools upon Achievement and Attendance." *Educational Administration and Supervision*, 1958, *44*, 191–198.

Eysenck, H. J. "An Exercise in Mega-Silliness." *American Psychologist*, 1978, *33*, 517.

Feldt, L. S., and Mahmoud, M. W. "Power Function Charts for Specification of Sample Size in Analysis of Variance." *Psychometrika*, 1958, *23*, 335–353.

Felice, L. G., and Richardson, R. L. *The Effects of Busing and School Desegregation on Majority and Minority Student Dropout Rates: An Evaluation of School Socioeconomic Composition and Teachers' Expectations*. Waco, Texas: Baylor University Press, 1976.

Gallo, P. S., Jr. "Meta-Analysis—A Mixed Metaphor?" *American Psychologist*, 1978, *33*, 515–517.

Gardner, B. B., Wright, B. D., and Dee, R. *The Effect of Busing Black Ghetto Children into White Suburban Schools*. Chicago: Catholic School Board, 1970. (ED 048 389)

Geiger, G. O. "Effects of Desegregation on Classroom Achievement." Unpublished doctoral dissertation, University of South Carolina, 1968.

Gilbert, J. P., McPeek, B., and Mosteller, F. "Progress in Surgery and Anesthesia: Benefits and Risks of Innovative Therapy." In J. P. Bunker, B. A. Barnes, and F. Mosteller (Eds.), *Costs, Risks, and Benefits of Surgery*. New York: Oxford University Press, 1977.

Glass, G. V. "Primary, Secondary, and Meta-Analysis of Research." *Educational Researcher*, 1976, *5*, 3–8.

Glass, G. V. "Integrating Findings: The Meta-Analysis of Research." In L. S. Shulman (Ed.), *Review of Research in Education*. Vol. 5. Itasca, Ill.: Peacock, 1977.

Glass, G. V. "Reply to Mansfield and Busse." *Educational Researcher*, 1978, *7*, 3.

Glass, G. V., McGaw, B., and Smith, M. L. *Meta-Analysis in Social Research*. Beverly Hills, Calif.: Sage, 1981.

Glass, G. V., and Smith, M. L. "Reply to Eysenck." *American Psychologist*, 1978, *33*, 517.

Hayden, J. E. "An Analysis of the Grade Point Averages of Black Bused and Nonbused Students at a Desegregated High School." Unpublished doctoral dissertation, University of Louisville, 1976.

Hedges, L. V. "Distribution Theory for Glass's Estimator of Effect Size and Related Estimators." *Journal of Educational Statistics,* 1981, *6,* 107–128.

Hedges, L. V. "Estimation of Effect Size from a Series of Independent Experiments." *Psychological Bulletin,* 1982, *92,* 490–499.

Hunter, J. E., Schmidt, F. L., and Jackson, G. *Meta-Analysis: Cumulating Research Findings Across Studies.* Beverly Hills, Calif.: Sage, 1982.

Hyde, J. S. "How Large Are Cognitive Gender Differences? A Meta-Analysis Using W^2 and *d.*" *American Psychologist,* 1981, *36,* 892–901.

Jackson, G. B. "Methods for Integrative Reviews." *Review of Educational Research,* 1980, *50,* 438–460.

Landman, J. T., and Dawes, R. "Psychotherapy Outcome: Smith and Glass's Conclusions Stand Up Under Scrutiny." *American Psychologist,* 1982, *37* (5), 504–516.

Lemke, E. A. "The Effects of Busing on the Achievement of White and Black Students." *Educational Studies,* 1979, *9,* 401–405.

Light, R. J., and Smith, P. V. "Accumulating Evidence: Procedures for Resolving Contradictions Among Different Research Studies." *Harvard Educational Review,* 1971, *41,* 429–471.

Lord, C., Ross, L., and Leper, M. "Biased Assimilation and Attitude Polarizations: The Effects of Prior Theories on Subsequently Considered Evidence." *Journal of Personality and Social Psychology,* 1979, *37,* 2098–2109.

McPartland, J. "The Relative Influence of School and of Classroom Desegregation on the Academic Achievement of Ninth-Grade Negro Students." *Journal of Social Issues,* 1969, *25* (3), 93–102.

Mahard, R. E., and Crain, R. L. "High School Racial Composition and the Academic Achievement and College Attendance of Hispanic Students." Paper presented at the annual American Sociological Association meetings, New York, August 1980.

Mahoney, M. "Publication Prejudices: An Experimental Study of Confirmatory Bias in the Peer Review System." *Cognitive Therapy and Research,* 1977, *1,* 161–175.

Mansfield, R. S., and Busse, T. V. "Meta-Analysis of Research: A Rejoinder to Glass." *Educational Researcher,* 1977, *6,* 3.

Merchant, J. N. "A Comparative Study of the Academic Achievement of Selected Negro and White Students in Desegregated Classrooms." Unpublished doctoral dissertation, East Texas State University, 1969.

Moorehead, N. F. "The Effects of School Integration on Intelligence Test Scores of Negro Children." Unpublished doctoral dissertation, Mississippi State University, 1972.

Morrison, G. A., Jr. "An Analysis of Academic Achievement Trends for Anglo American, Mexican American, and Negro American Students in a Desegregated School Environment." Unpublished doctoral dissertation, University of Houston, 1972.

Orwin, R. G., and Cordray, D. S. "The Effects of Deficient Reporting on Meta-Analysis: A Conceptual Framework and Reanalysis." Unpublished manuscript, Northwestern University, 1983.

Phillips, L. W., and Bianchi, U. "Desegregation, Reading Achievement, and Problem Behavior in Two Elementary Schools." *Urban Education,* 1975, *11* (4), 325–329.

Prichard, P. N. "Effects of Desegregation on Student Success in the Chapel Hill School." *Integrated Education,* 1969, *7,* 33–38.

Purl, M. C., and Dawson, J. A. *The Achievement of Students in Primary Grades After Seven Years of Desegregation.* Riverside, Calif.: Riverside Unified School District, 1973.

Rosenthal, R. "Summarizing Significance Levels." In R. Rosenthal (Ed.), *Quantitative Assessment of Research Domains.* New Directions for Methodology of Social and Behavioral Sciences, no. 5. San Francisco: Jossey-Bass, 1980.

Rossi, P. H., and Williams, W. *Evaluating Social Programs.* New York: Seminar Press, 1972.

Sacramento City Unified School District. *Focus on Reading and Math, 1970–1971: An Evaluation Report on a Program of Compensatory Education (ESEA Title 1).* Sacramento, Calif.: Sacramento City Unified School District, 1971.

Saxe, L. "Meta-analysis." Paper presented at the annual meeting of the American Public Health Association Convention, Dallas, November 1983.

Smith, M. L. "Publication Bias and Meta-Analysis." *Evaluation in Education,* 1980, *4,* 22–24.

Smith, M. L., and Glass, G. V. "Meta-Analysis of Psychotherapy Outcome Studies." *American Psychologist,* 1977, *32,* 752–760.

Staines, G. L. "The Strategic Combination Argument." In W. Leinfellner and E. Kohler (Eds.), *Developments in the Methodology of Social Science.* Dordecht, Holland: Reidel, 1974.

Teele, J. E. *Evaluating School Busing: A Case Study of Boston's Operation Exodus.* New York: Praeger, 1973.

Weinberg, M. *Minority Students: A Research Appraisal.* Washington, D.C.: U.S. Department of Health, Education, and Welfare and National Institute of Education, 1977.

Wortman, P. M. "Evaluation Research: A Methodological Perspective." *Annual Review of Psychology,* 1983, *34,* 223–260.

Wortman, P. M., and Bryant, F. B. "School Desegregation and Black Student Achievement: An Integrative Review." *Sociological Methods & Research,* forthcoming.

Wortman, P. M., Reichardt, C. S., and St. Pierre, R. G. "The First Year of the Education Voucher Demonstration: A Secondary Analysis of Student Achievement Test Scores." *Evaluation Quarterly,* 1978, *2,* 193–214.

Wortman, P. M., and Yeaton, W. H. "Synthesis of Results in Controlled Trials of Coronary Artery Bypass Graft Surgery." In R. J. Light (Ed.), *Evaluation Studies Review Annual.* Vol. 8. Beverly Hills, Calif.: Sage, 1983.

Fred B. Bryant is assistant professor of social psychology at Loyola University of Chicago. His research interests include meta-analysis of quasi-experimental literatures and selection of appropriate evidence.

Paul M. Wortman is director of the Methodology and Evaluation Research Program in the Institute for Social Research and professor in the School of Public Health at the University of Michigan–Ann Arbor. His current research interests include research synthesis methods and medical technology assessment.

*Recent advances in statistical methods for meta-analysis help
reviewers to identify systematic variation in research results.*

Advances in Statistical Methods for Meta-Analysis

Larry V. Hedges

Meta-analysis makes use of statistical methods to describe the results of a
number of research studies. Typically, the results of each study are summarized by an index of effect size. These indices can then be averaged to obtain
an overall estimate of the magnitude of effects. Other statistical analyses can
also be performed to study the variation of effect sizes across studies. Until
recently, meta-analysis used such conventional statistical methods as multiple
regression analysis and analysis of variance to analyze effect size data. Such
use seemed at first to be an innocuous extension of statistical methods to a new
situation. However, recent research has demonstrated that the use of such statistical procedures as analysis of variance and regression analysis cannot be
justified for meta-analysis. Fortunately, some new statistical procedures have
been designed specifically for meta-analysis. These new procedures exploit the
properties of effect sizes to provide analyses that avoid the difficulties created
for meta-analysis by conventional statistical procedures.

This chapter introduces some of the new statistical procedures that
were recently developed for the analysis of effect size data. The first section
analyzes the goals of statistical procedures for research synthesis. The next section shows that conventional statistical methods cannot accomplish some of

The research reported in this chapter was supported by the Spencer Foundation.

W. H. Yeaton, P. M. Wortman (Eds.). *Issues in Data Synthesis.*
New Directions for Program Evaluation, no. 24. San Francisco: Jossey-Bass, December 1984.

these goals. The third section examines the basic statistical sampling properties of effect sizes, and develops some analogues to analysis of variance and multiple regression analysis for effect sizes. The fourth section discusses the importance of tests for the consistency of effect sizes in interpreting the results of meta-analysis. The fifth section discusses some of the problems in obtaining well-specified models for meta-analysis. Finally, an appendix provides detail on some statistical computations.

Goals of Statistical Procedures in Research Synthesis

Before addressing any specific statistical procedures for the quantitative synthesis of research, it will be useful to consider what can be expected of statistical analysis in the best possible situation. Perhaps the simplest situation for the synthesis of research results is one in which the raw data from several experiments can be pooled directly. For example, suppose that we have a series of k two-group experiments, each of which uses an experimental–control group design to investigate the effects of a given treatment. Let us assume that each study uses the same instrument and the same sampling plan to measure the normally distributed outcome variable, so that the within-group population variances of the outcome scores are identical. We can even arbitrarily set the common within-group variances to one, although it is not necessary to do so.

The situation just defined is one in which the raw data from all the individuals in all the studies are directly comparable. Consequently, the outcome scores of all the individuals can be combined and analyzed in one large statistical analysis. In this situation, most social scientists know how to proceed. Most investigators would use the data from all individuals in one large $2 \times k$ (two treatments $\times$ k studies) analysis of variance. In the idealized case just described, the assumptions of analysis of variance will be exactly met.

What will the investigator learn from the analysis of variance? There are three omnibus F tests in the textbook analysis. The F test for the main effect of studies is relatively uninteresting. It tests whether the value of the outcome variable averaged over both experimental and control groups differs across studies. The other two F tests are more interesting. The F test for the treatment factor tests whether the treatment group outperforms the control group on the average across all k experiments. The F test for the treatment-by-studies interaction tests whether the treatment effect is consistent across studies. The interpretation of the statistical analysis rests largely on the second and third tests. A large treatment effect with a negligible interaction is easy to interpret: The treatment produces a large consistent effect across studies. If the interaction is not negligible, then interpretation becomes more complicated, because interaction suggests that the treatment effect is larger in some studies than it is in others. Thus, any statements about the main effect must be qualified by the fact that treatment effects vary significantly across studies.

If a significant interaction is found, most investigators will probably begin to look for reasons why the treatment effect varies across studies. Variations in treatment, experimental procedure, conditions of measurement, or sample composition can all figure in explanations of variations in treatment effect. If a suitable explanatory variable can be found, it can be entered into the statistical analysis as a blocking factor. By an appropriate F test, further analysis could then reveal whether the new factor accounted for a significant amount of variation in the treatment effects and whether variations in the treatment effect remained substantial across studies within levels of the new factor. That is, we can test whether a proposed explanatory factor succeeds in "explaining" — that is, in removing — the variations in treatment effect across studies. This test is conceptually analogous to the original test for the treatment-by-studies interaction.

Thus, in the best possible case, where data from all studies can be combined directly, statistical analysis has four features: First, the average treatment effect can be estimated and tested across all studies. Second, the consistency of treatment effects can also be tested via the treatment-by-studies interaction. Third, if explanatory variables corresponding to differences among studies are used to explain variations in treatment effect, the effect of those explanatory variables can be tested. Fourth, the significance of variation in treatment effects across levels of the explanatory variables can be tested to determine whether all variations in treatment effect have been explained.

In evaluating statistical methods for research synthesis, it is useful to ask which features of the best-case analysis just described are available for the analysis that is proposed. Statistical methods now exist that provide all the advantages of best-case analysis for any meta-analysis. These methods allow the meta-analyst to answer essentially the same questions that he or she would ask if it were possible to combine the raw data from all the studies directly. Conventional statistical procedures fail to answer one or more of the questions of interest. Moreover, use of some conventional analyses for effect size data frequently involves serious violations of the assumptions of these techniques. Thus, use of conventional statistical procedures in meta-analysis is problematic for both statistical and conceptual reasons. Let us now turn to the specific problems of conventional statistical procedures in meta-analysis.

Conventional Analyses for Effect Size Data

The use of conventional analyses for research synthesis has been greatly influenced by the pioneering work of Glass (1976). He suggested combining the results of studies by first calculating an estimate of effect size g, which is the standardized difference between the experimental and control group means; that is,

$$g = (\overline{Y}E - \overline{Y}C)/S.$$

The estimates of effect size from different studies are standardized so that they exist in effect on the same scale. As a result, the meta-analyst can combine these estimates across studies or treat the effect sizes as raw data for analysis of variance or multiple linear regression that relate characteristics of studies to treatment effects (Glass and others, 1981).

Table 1 summarizes the results of six studies of the effects of open and traditional education on student cooperativeness (Hedges, 1982b). Conventional statistical analysis would calculate the average of the g values to obtain $\bar{g} = .168$. The investigator would probably conclude that the effect of open education on cooperativeness was not statistically significantly different from zero (the one-sample t test for $\bar{g}$ is $t(5) = .819, p > .25$). The investigator could also test for the existence of a relation between degree of treatment fidelity and effect size by using a t test or an analysis of variance to determine whether the average effect size for the studies where treatment fidelity was low differed from the average effect size of the studies where treatment fidelity was high. Conventional analysis of variance would show that the average effect sizes of the two groups did not differ significantly: $F(1,4) = 4.15, p > .10$. We shall see later that use of statistical procedures designed specifically for meta-analysis would cause all these conclusions to be modified.

Conceptual Problems with Conventional Analyses. Let us now compare the conventional analysis with the best-case analysis in which all the raw data can be directly combined. In our idealized best case, the treatment effect (mean difference) corresponds directly to the effect size for each study. In the conventional analysis, the effect sizes can be averaged to obtain an estimate of the average treatment effect. Similarly, the effect of any particular explanatory variable can be tested by using that variable as a blocking factor in an analysis of variance or as a predictor in a regression analysis in which the effect size is the dependent variable. Thus, the conventional effect size analysis has two features of the best-case analysis.

Table 1. Effect Sizes from Six Studies of the Effects of
Open Education on Cooperativeness

Study	Treatment Fidelity	n^E	n^C	g	d	v	w	wd	wd^2
1	Low	30	30	.181	.179	.0669	14.940	2.669	.4768
2	Low	30	30	− .521	− .514	.0689	14.520	− 7.467	3.8396
3	Low	280	290	− .131	− .131	.0070	142.152	− 18.597	2.4330
4	High	6	11	.959	.910	.2819	3.547	3.228	2.9386
5	High	44	40	.097	.096	.0478	20.928	2.011	.1933
6	High	37	55	.425	.421	.0462	21.657	9.127	3.8467
				Totals			217.745	− 9.028	13.7282

Source: Hedges, 1982b.

At the same time, however, the conventional analysis lacks two important features of the best-case analysis. First, conventional analysis cannot test the consistency of effect sizes directly across studies. That is, there is no analogue in conventional effect size analysis to the test for treatment-by-study interactions. The conventional analysis for testing systematic variation among k effect sizes has $(k-1)$ degrees of freedom for systematic variation among effect sizes and one degree of freedom for the grand mean. No degrees of freedom are left for estimation of error or nonsystematic variation. Consequently, it is impossible in the conventional framework to construct a test that can determine whether the systematic variation in k effect sizes is larger than the nonsystematic variation exhibited by those effect sizes.

It is possible in the conventional analysis to construct a test for differences among the average effect sizes of two or more groups of studies, as long as at least one of the groups contains two or more effect sizes. The multiple effect sizes within these groups serve as replicates from which an estimate of unsystematic variance can be obtained. The test itself is constructed by comparing systematic variance among group mean effect sizes with the unsystematic variance of effect sizes within groups. However, such a test is both conceptually and statistically perilous. How does the analyst know that the effect sizes vary nonsystematically within the groups? If the wrong groups are chosen, considerable systematic variance may be pooled into the estimate of error variance. This issue lay at the core of Presby's (1978) criticism of Smith and Glass's meta-analysis of psychotherapy outcome studies (1977). She argued that their analysis of differences among types of psychotherapy was flawed because the categories of therapy that they used were overly broad; they included considerable systematic variation. The effect of pooling systematic variation into estimates of error terms is well known to statisticians. It decreases the sensitivity of the statistical test for systematic variation. The conceptual problem that threatens the conventional analysis is that the analyst can never know how much of the variation among effect sizes is systematic.

Precisely the same problem plagues attempts to construct a test for the variation in effect sizes that remains after an explanatory variable has been applied. If the analyst tries to explain variation in effect sizes by grouping studies with similar characteristics or by using a linear predictor, he or she still has no way of assessing whether the remaining variation among effect sizes is systematic or random.

Statistical Problems with Conventional Analyses. Use of conventional statistical methods to analyze effect sizes or correlation coefficients is also problematic for purely statistical reasons. Conventional statistical procedures— t tests, analysis of variance, multiple regression analysis—rely on parametric assumptions about the data. All these procedures require the unsystematic variance associated with individual observations to be the same—the so-called homoscedasticity assumption. That is, if we think of each observation as composed of a systematic part and an error part, then the errors for all observations must be equally variable. In analysis of variance, we are accustomed to verifying that within-cell variances are reasonably similar in value for all cells in the design. In regression analysis, we can check this assumption by determining whether the residual variance about the regression line is reasonably constant for all values of the predictor variable.

In the case of estimates of effect magnitude (either correlation coefficients or effect sizes), the unsystematic variance of an observation can be calculated analytically. In fact, the unsystematic variance of estimates of effect size is proportional to $\frac{1}{n}$, where n is the sample size of the study on which the estimate is based. Thus, if studies have different sample sizes, which is usually the case, the effect size estimates will have different error variances. If the sample sizes of the studies subjected to meta-analysis vary widely, so will the error variances. In many meta-analyses, it is not unusual for the range of sample sizes to be on the order of fifty to one. In these cases, the error variances are substantially heterogeneous.

How can we deal with this problem? The effects of heterogeneity of variance on analysis of variance F tests have been studied extensively (for example, Glass and others, 1972). Heterogeneous variances have been shown to have very small effects on the validity of F tests in conventional analysis of variance. However, the situation in research synthesis is usually quite different. Studies of the effects of heterogeneity of variance in analysis of variance usually give a different variance to one or more groups in the design. Thus, every observation in the same group has the same variance, and there are at most two to three different variances in the entire experiment. In the case of research synthesis, the heterogeneity is usually more pronounced. Every observation—that is, every study—can have a different variance. Moreover, the range of variances studied in connection with the robustness of conventional F tests is usually rather limited, often less than five to one. The studies that have examined the effects of very wide ranges of variances have found that the F test is not necessarily robust to substantial heterogeneity of variance. For example, Glass and others (1972) note that when the ratio of variances is five to one and the sample sizes are unequal, then the actual significance level of an F test can be six times as large as the nominal significance level—.30 instead of .05.

Thus, the violation of the assumption of analysis of variance and regression analysis about homogeneity of variance is severe in research synthesis. Moreover, the particular nature of this violation has not been extensively studied. There is very little reason to believe that the usual robustness of the F test will somehow prevail. The statistical problem created by violation of the assumptions of conventional statistical procedures, combined with the potential problem of bias due to pooling of systematic variation in estimates of error variance, raises severe questions about the validity of conventional statistical procedures in meta-analysis. There does not appear to be any rigorously defensible argument for the use of conventional t tests, analysis of variance, or regression analysis to analyze effect sizes or correlations.

Modern Statistical Methods for Effect Sizes

Modern statistical methods for the analysis of effect sizes overcome both the conceptual and the statistical problems that plague conventional statistical analyses. The new methods are designed specifically for effect size data, but they can be calculated from standard packaged statistical programs, such as the Statistical Analysis System (SAS) or the Statistical Package for the Social Sciences (SPSS). In the remainder of this section, the basic properties of effect sizes on which these new methods are based are described, and the systematic and unsystematic components of sample effect sizes are distinguished. Properties of unsystematic sampling variation are used first to construct statistical tests for average effect size, then to develop an analogue to analysis of variance for effect sizes.

Properties of Effect Sizes. For meta-analysis, the effect size or standardized mean difference is the fundamental quantity in between-group studies. Let us begin by focusing on the effect size for a single study. Glass (1976) defined effect size as the difference between the experimental group mean and the control group mean, divided by the standard deviation of the control group:

$$g = (\overline{Y}E - \overline{Y}C)/S.$$

If there is no concrete reason to believe that the within-group variances differ, the standard deviation of the control group can be replaced by a pooled within-group standard deviation defined by

$$S^2 = [(nE - 1)(SE)^2 + (nC - 1)(SC)^2]/(nE + nC - 2)$$

The pooled standard deviation has desirable statistical properties such as small sampling error (Hedges, 1981), and when effect sizes must be derived from test statistics it is often the only standard deviation that is available.

The effect size estimate g can be decomposed into a systematic part, which reflects a true or population treatment effect, and an unsystematic part, which reflects sampling error of the individual scores used to calculate the effect size. The systematic part is called the *population effect size:*

(1) $$\delta = (\mu^E - \mu^C)/\sigma,$$

where μ^E and μ^C are the population means of scores in the experimental and the control group respectively, and σ is the population standard deviation within the groups of the study. I use the Greek letters δ, μ^E, μ^C, and σ to indicate that the population effect size δ is a population parameter defined by population parameters μE, μC, and σ of the observations in the study. The unsystematic part of the effect size estimate g is the sampling error $\epsilon = g - \delta$. Thus, the decomposition of g follows directly as

(2) $$g = \delta + \epsilon$$

This decomposition is important, because it highlights an important feature of meta-analysis. That is, all systematic relationships in meta-analysis are relationships involving δ, the population effect size. The sampling error ϵ is nonsystematic by definition, and therefore it has no systematic relationship to anything. The estimate of effect size g is useful only because it provides information about δ. Thus, if the meta-analyst uses regression or analysis of variance to study the relationship between degree of treatment implementation and effect size, the systematic relationship is between degree of treatment implementation and population effect size. This fundamental decomposition of the sample estimate of effect size into systematic and unsystematic components is essential in statistical analysis for effect sizes.

The simplest statistical question in effect size analyses concerns the properties of g. Since g is of interest only because it provides information about δ, we need to ask whether g is a good estimator of δ. The answer is that g is a slightly biased estimator of δ that tends to overestimate δ for small samples. A simple correction gives an unbiased estimator of δ (Hedges, 1981). This unbiased estimator, d, is obtained by multiplying g by a constant that depends on the sample size in the study. That is,

(3) $$d = c_n g = c_n(\overline{Y}E - \overline{Y}C)/S$$

where the values of c_n are given to a very good approximation by

(4) $$c_n = 1 - \frac{3}{4nE + 4nC - 9}$$

Note that c_n is very close to one for all but very small values of nE and nC. Consequently, g is almost unbiased except in very small samples. However, the correction for bias is easy to apply, and the unbiased estimator has theoretical advantages. Consequently, there is little reason not to use the bias correction routinely. The remainder of this discussion uses the notation d for the estimator of effect size and assumes that the bias correction has been used. The correction for bias is analogous to the correction for the sample estimate of variance. The definition of the population variance has an n in the denominator. Using $n - 1$ in the denominator of the sample variance is equivalent to multiplying the population definition by the constant $\frac{n}{(n-1)}$ to obtain an unbiased estimate.

An understanding of the sampling properties of the estimator d of effect size is essential for the construction of statistical tests and estimation procedures for effect sizes. The sampling properties of d can be derived analytically for the case in which the assumptions of the t test are met by the observations in a study. That is, if the t or F test that the primary researcher has used is valid, then the properties of the sampling error ϵ of the effect size are completely determined. Hedges (1981) showed that d is approximately normally distributed with mean δ and variance

$$(5) \qquad v = \frac{n^E + n^C}{n^E n^C} + \frac{d^2}{2(n^E + n^C)}$$

Alternatively, we could say that $\epsilon = d - \delta$ is normally distributed with the mean zero and variance given in equation 5. If the experimental and control groups of a study are equal in size — that is, if $n^E = n^C = n$ — then the variance becomes

$$v = \frac{2}{n}\left(1 + \frac{d^2}{8}\right)$$

The variance of d is completely determined by the sample sizes and the value of d. Consequently, it is possible to determine the sampling variance of d from a single observation. The ability to determine the nonsystematic variance of d (the variance of ϵ) from a single observation of d is the key to modern statistical methods for meta-analysis. This relationship allows the meta-analyst to use all the degrees of freedom among different d values for estimating systematic effects while still providing a way of estimating the unsystematic variance needed to construct statistical tests.

Combining Estimates of Effect Sizes for a Set of Studies. One of the first statistical questions that arises is how to combine estimates of effect size. Suppose that a series of k studies with sample sizes $n_1^E, n_1^C, \ldots, n_k^E, n_k^C$ provides k independent effect size estimates (that is, effect size estimates based on independent samples) $d_1, \ldots, d_k$. One way of combining the estimates is simply to take the average $\bar{d}$. The most precise combination, however, is a weighted average that takes the variances $v_1, \ldots, v_k$ of $d_1, \ldots, d_k$ into account. This weighted average, denoted $d.$, is defined as follows:

$$(6) \qquad d. = \sum_{i=1}^{k} w_i d_i / \sum_{i=1}^{k} w_i$$

where

$$(7) \qquad w_i = 1/v_i = \frac{2(n_i^E + n_i^C)n_i^E n_i^C}{2(n_i^E + n_i^C)^2 + n_i^E n_i^C d_i^2}$$

If all k studies share a common population effect size δ, the weighted mean $d.$ is approximately normally distributed with a mean of δ and a variance of

$$(8) \qquad v. = 1/\sum_{i=1}^{k} w_i$$

Consequently, if it is reasonable to believe that a set of studies shares a common effect size δ, then a $100(1 - \alpha)$ percent confidence interval for δ is given by

$$d. - z_\alpha \sqrt{v.} \ < \delta < d. + z_\alpha \sqrt{v.}$$

where z_α is the 100α percent two-tailed critical value of the standard normal distribution. If the confidence interval does not include zero or, alternatively, if

$$\left| d. / \sqrt{v.} \right| > z_\alpha$$

then the hypothesis that $\delta = 0$ is rejected at significance level α.

In our example, the effect size estimates from $k = 6$ studies are given in Table 1. The variances v_i, the weights w_i, and $w_i d_i$ are also given for each study. Thus, $d.$ is calculated from the totals (sums) or w_i and $w_i d_i$ values as $d. = .041 = -9.028/217.745$. The variance $v.$ of $d.$ is calculated from the total of the w_i values as $v. = 1/217.745 = .004592$. To test that the average effect size is zero, compute $\left| d./\sqrt{v.} \right| = .41/.06776 = .605$, which is not significant.

Testing Homogeneity of Effect Size. Combining estimates of effect size across studies is reasonable if the studies have a common population effect size δ. In this case, the estimates of effect size differ only by unsystematic sampling error. However, if the studies do not share a common underlying effect size, it can be misleading to combine estimates of effect size across studies. For example, if half of the studies had a large positive population effect size and half of the studies had a negative population effect size of equal magnitude, then the average—zero—is not representative of the effect size in any of the studies. The obvious question at this point is, How do we determine whether population effect sizes are relatively constant across studies? That is, how do we test for treatment-by-study interactions?

A test for homogeneity of effect size has been given by Hedges (1982a) and independently by Rosenthal and Rubin (1982). The test involves computing

$$(9) \qquad H_T = \sum_{i=1}^{k} w_i (d_i - d.)^2$$

where $w_i = 1/v_i$ is the weight given in equation 7 and $d.$ is the weighted mean given by equation 6. The H_T statistic is simply the weighted sum of squares of the estimates $d_1, \ldots, d_k$ of effect size about the weighted mean $d.$. If all studies share a common effect size δ, then the statistic H_T has approximately a chi square distribution with $(k - 1)$ degrees of freedom. Thus, the test for treatment-by-study interaction rejects homogeneity of effect size at significance level α if H exceeds the $100(1 - \alpha)$ percent critical value of the chi square distribution with $(k - 1)$ degrees of freedom.

Returning to our example, we can compute H_T to test whether the six studies summarized in Table 1 have homogeneous effect sizes. Using the totals (sums) of w_i, $w_i d_i^2$ from Table 1 and equation 12 from the appendix to this chapter, we compute H_T as $H_T = 13.728 - (-9.028)^2/217.745 = 13.384$. Because H_T exceeds 11.1 — the 95 percent critical value of the chi square distribution with five degrees of freedom — we can reject the hypothesis that the six studies share a common underlying effect size. Thus, there is systematic variation among these effect sizes that needs to be explained, and any attempt to summarize these studies by a single average effect size is likely to be misleading.

An Analogue to Analysis of Variance for Effect Sizes. When effect sizes are not homogeneous across studies — that is, when treatment-by-study interactions are present — the meta-analyst may want to explain variations in effect sizes by variations in characteristics of studies. One way of proceeding is to group studies that share characteristics that can influence effect size. Thus, the meta-analyst would seek to create groupings in which the variability of effect sizes was small. If the raw data from all studies could be combined directly, the grouping factor could be introduced into an analysis of variance, and an *F* test could be used to test the significance of between-group variation.

A statistical procedure that permits the same kind of analysis for effect sizes was introduced by Hedges (1982b). This analogue to analysis of variance for effect sizes permits the meta-analyst to test the significance of variations between groups of effect sizes. It also permits the investigator to test whether the remaining variation within groups of effect sizes is significant. Thus, it permits the meta-analyst to determine whether the explanatory grouping variable adequately explains the treatment-by-study interaction.

The analysis of variance for effect sizes involves a partitioning of the overall homogeneity statistic H_T given in equation 9 into two independent homogeneity statistics: H_B, reflecting between-group homogeneity, and H_W, reflecting within-group homogeneity. These homogeneity statistics are related by the algebraic identity $H_T = H_B + H_W$, which is analogous to the partitioning of sums of squares in analysis of variance.

The between-group homogeneity statistic H_B is a weighted sum of squares of weighted group mean effect size estimates about the overall weighted mean effect size. That is,

(10)
$$H_B = \Sigma w_{j\cdot}(d_{j\cdot} - d_{\cdot\cdot})^2$$

where $d_{\cdot\cdot}$ is the overall weighted mean across all studies ignoring groupings, $d_{j\cdot}$ is the weighted mean of effect size estimates in the jth group, and $w_{j\cdot} = 1/v_{j\cdot}$ is the reciprocal of the variance of $d_{j\cdot}$. Here, the weighted means and their variances are calculated using equation 6 and equation 8. The between-group homogeneity statistic H_B is analogous to the *F* statistic used for testing between-group differences in the conventional analysis of variance.

When there are p groups, the statistic H_B has approximately a chi square distribution with $(p - 1)$ degrees of freedom when there is no variation between group mean effect sizes. Thus, the test for variation in effect sizes between groups compares H_B with the $100(1 - \alpha)$ percent critical value of the chi square distribution with $(p - 1)$ degrees of freedom. If H_B exceeds the critical value, the variation between group mean effect sizes is significant at level α.

The within-group homogeneity statistic is the sum of the homogeneity statistics (equation 9) calculated for each of the p groups separately. That is,

$$(11) \qquad H_W = H_{W1} + \ldots + H_{Wp}$$

where $H_{W1}, \ldots, H_{Wp}$ are the homogeneity statistics (equation 9) calculated as if each group were an entire collection of studies. Whenever a group contains more than one study, the within-group homogeneity statistic for the group can be used to test the homogeneity of effect sizes within that group. If there is only one effect size estimate in a group, then $H_{Wi} = 0$ for that group. The total H_W provides an overall test of homogeneity of effect size within the groups of studies.

If a total of k studies is divided into $p < k$ groups, then H_W has a chi square distribution with $(k - p)$ degrees of freedom when the effect sizes are homogeneous within groups. The test for homogeneity of effect size within groups at significance level α consists of comparing H_W with the $100(1 - \alpha)$ percent critical value of the chi square distribution with $(k - p)$ degrees of freedom. The homogeneity of effect sizes within groups is rejected if H_W exceeds the critical value.

Let us suppose that the meta-analyst "explains" the variations in effect sizes by finding that effect sizes are reasonably homogeneous within groups but that they differ between groups. If there are only two groups of studies, then a significant H_B statistic indicates that there is a significant difference between their population effect sizes. If there are more than two groups, then the meta-analyst may want to use comparisons or contrasts analogous to those in analysis of variance to explore the differences among effect sizes for the different groups. Procedures for testing comparisons among the effect sizes of different groups follow from the properties of $d.$; they have been discussed by Hedges (1982b).

For the six studies summarized in Table 1, we calculated H_T and found that they did not share a single common effect size. If we now subdivide the studies into two groups — one with low treatment fidelity (studies one through three) and one with high treatment fidelity (studies four through six) — we calculate the within-class fit statistics $H_{W1} = 3.560$ for studies where treatment fidelity is low and $H_{W2} = 2.504$ for studies where treatment fidelity is high. Hence, the total within-class fit statistic is $H_W = H_{W1} + H_{W2} = 3.560 + 2.504 = 6.064$, which is much less than 9.49, the 95 percent critical value of the chi square distribution with four degrees of freedom. Hence, the effect sizes within the two groups are homogeneous. Calculating H_B, we obtain $H_B = H_T - H_W = 13.394 - 6.064 = 7.320$. Comparing 7.320 with 3.84, the 95 percent critical value of the chi square distribution with one degree of freedom, we see that the difference between the effect sizes in the two groups is statistically significant. The weighted average effect size for the low fidelity studies is $d_{1.} = -.136$, which is not statistically significant at the $\alpha = .05$ level. The weighted average effect size for the high fidelity studies is $d_{2.} = .311$, which is statistically significant at the $\alpha = .05$ level.

It is instructive to compare the results of the analysis described here with the results of conventional analysis. Conventional analysis found a small and nonsignificant average effect size for all studies. Conventional analysis also suggested that the effect sizes of studies where treatment fidelity was low did not differ from those of studies where treatment fidelity was high. Thus, conventional analysis concluded that the overall effect was small and that treatment fidelity had no effect on the results of the individual studies.

Analysis with the new methods described in this chapter reached different conclusions. First, the test of overall homogeneity of effect size showed that the studies did not produce consistent results. This suggested that no single estimate was adequate to describe the results of all six studies. The analysis of variance for effect sizes showed that the two groups of studies produced significantly different average effect sizes. Moreover, the analysis showed that the effect sizes were homogeneous within the two groups. Thus, the results of the analysis of variance for effect sizes suggest that there is a consistent but negligible effect among the studies with low treatment fidelity and a consistent, statistically significant positive effect among the studies with high treatment fidelity.

An Analogue to Multiple Regression Analysis for Effect Sizes. In many research reviews, it is desirable to investigate the relationship between variations in one or more quantitative explanatory variables and variations in effect size. For example, Smith and Glass (1977) used conventional multiple regression analysis in their meta-analysis of psychotherapy outcome studies to determine the relationship between several coded characteristics of studies, such as type of therapy, duration of therapy, and internal validity, and effect size. The same authors have used this method in other meta-analyses (Glass and Smith, 1979; Smith and Glass, 1980). Conventional multiple regression analysis cannot be used with effect sizes, but an analogue can. This analogue, which uses a weighted regression procedure, provides a way of estimating and testing the relationship between several predictor variables and effect size. It also provides a way of testing whether the regression model is adequately specified, that is, whether significant systematic variation in effect sizes remains unexplained by the data analysis model. A complete set of formulas, derivations, and computational procedures has been given by Hedges (1982c), but the computational procedure itself can be explained quite easily without recourse to complicated formulas.

Suppose that we have k independent effect size estimates $d_1, \ldots, d_k$ and p predictor variables $X_1, \ldots, X_p$ that we believe to be related to effect sizes. Under the data analysis model described here, the systematic part of the effect sizes (the population effect sizes) $\delta_1, \ldots, \delta_k$ is determined as a linear function of the values of the predictor variables $X_1, \ldots, X_p$. That is,

$$\delta_i = \beta_0 + \beta_1 x_{ip} + \ldots + \beta_p X_{ip},$$

where $\beta_0, \beta_1, \ldots, \beta_p$ are unknown regression coefficients, and x_{ij} is the value of the jth predictor variable for the ith study. One object of statistical analysis is to use the observed estimates of effect size $d_1, \ldots, d_k$ and the values of the predictor variables to estimate the relationship between $X_1, \ldots, X_p$ and the effect sizes, that is, to estimate the unknown regression coefficients. Another object of this analysis is to test whether the regression model is correctly specified, that is, whether significant systematic variation remains unexplained by the regression model.

The easiest way to compute the estimates of regression coefficients and the test for model misspecification is to use a packaged computer program, such as the Statistical Analysis System Procedure General Linear Model (SAS Proc GLM), that can perform weighted regression analyses. It can be proved that the best estimate of regression coefficients can be obtained by using a weighted multiple regression of effect size estimates on the predictor variables, weighting each effect size by $w_i = 1/v_i$ given in equation 7. This is accomplished by creating a variable W whose value for each effect size equals the reciprocal of the variance of that effect size. The multiple regression is then run in the usual way, except that the variable W is specified as the weighting variable.

The output of the weighted regression analysis gives the estimates $\hat{\beta}_0$, $\hat{\beta}_1, \ldots, \hat{\beta}_p$ of the regression coefficients directly. The standard errors and the t or F tests printed by the packaged computer program are incorrect, and they should be ignored. The correct standard errors for $\hat{\beta}_0, \ldots, \hat{\beta}_p$ are given by the square roots of the diagonal elements of the $X'WX$ inverse matrix printed by the weighted regression program. The correct test for the significance of β_j uses the fact that

$$z_j = \hat{\beta}_j / \sqrt{S_{jj}}$$

is approximately a standard normal variable if $\beta_j = 0$, where S_{jj} is the correct standard error of β_j (the jth diagonal element of the $X'WX$ inverse matrix). Consequently, if $|z_j|$ exceeds the 100α percent critical value of the standard normal distribution, the hypothesis that $\beta_\sigma = 0$ is rejected at the significance level α.

If the number k of studies exceeds $(p + 1)$, the number of predictors plus the intercept, then a test for model specification is possible. The test uses the weighted sum of squares H_E about the regression line. Computer printouts sometimes term this statistic the *residual* or *error sum of squares*. When the population effect sizes are completely determined by the predictor variables — that is, when the regression model is correctly specified — then the statistic H_E has a chi square distribution with $(k - p - 1)$ degrees of freedom. Thus, the test for model specification at significance level α compares the error sum of squares H_E to the $100(1 - \alpha)$ percent critical value of the chi square distribution with $(k - p - 1)$ degrees of freedom. The model specification is rejected if H_E exceeds the critical value. Thus, the test for model specification is a test for greater than expected residual variation.

The Importance of Tests for Homogeneity and Model Specification

Some critics have argued that meta-analysis can lead to oversimplified conclusions about the effects of treatment because it condenses the results of a set of studies into a few parameter estimates. For example, Presby (1978) argued that even when studies were grouped according to variations in treatment, reviewers could reasonably disagree on the appropriate groupings. Grouping studies into overly broad categories and calculating a mean effect size for each category could wash out real variations among treatments within the categories. As a result, variations in treatment would appear to be unrelated, because the mean effect sizes for the categories did not differ. One obvious extension of this argument is that reviewers can reasonably disagree on explanatory variables that can be related to effect sizes. Hence, the failure of conventional analyses to find variables that are systematically related to effect size does not imply that the effect sizes are consistent across studies, since it can also imply that the reviewer has examined the wrong explanatory variables.

A related criticism is that the artifacts of a multitude of design flaws can cause the studies within a given set to give fundamentally different answers, that is, to have different population effect sizes (Eysenck, 1978). Any analysis of the effect sizes is therefore an analysis of estimates that are influenced by factors other than the true magnitude of the effect of treatment. The argument underlying this criticism is that flaws in the design or execution of studies can influence effect sizes.

Both criticisms imply the existence of treatment-by-study interactions—interactions that make the average or main effect of treatment difficult to interpret. The failure of conventional analysis to provide general tests for treatment-by-study interactions makes it vulnerable to such criticisms as those of Eysenck (1978) and Presby (1978). Statistical tests of the homogeneity of within-group effect size and tests for misspecification of multiple regression models can provide answers to such criticisms. More significantly, such tests provide the meta-analyst with concrete guidelines that he or she can use to judge whether the data have been adequately explained. In the simplest case, the meta-analyst summarizes the results of a set of studies by the average effect size estimate. Does this oversimplify the results of the individual studies? The test of homogeneity of effect size provides a method of testing empirically whether the variation in effect size estimates exceeds the variation that could be expected from chance alone. If the hypothesis of homogeneity is not rejected, the meta-analyst is in a strong position to reject the argument that the real variability of the studies in question has been obscured by coarse grouping. If the model of a single population effect size fits the data adequately, then the criterion of parsimony suggests that this model should be considered seriously.

Failure to reject the homogeneity of effect sizes for a set of studies does not necessarily disarm the criticism that the results of the studies are artifacts of design flaws. For example, if the studies in a set all share the same flaw, consistent results across the studies may be an artifact of that one flaw. That is, the same design flaw in all the studies may act to make the effect sizes in the studies consistently wrong as an estimate of the treatment effect. However, the studies may not all have the same flaws. If different studies with different design flaws all yield consistent results, it may be implausible to explain the consistency of their results as the result of consistent bias. Thus, the meta-analyst who finds consistency in research results and who knows the limitations of the individual studies is in a strong position to reject the argument that results are only as good as the data. It should be emphasized that careful examination of the individual research studies and some scrutiny of the attendant design problems are essential. Without such examination and such scrutiny, a single source of bias is a very real and plausible rival explanation for empirical consistency in research results.

When the meta-analyst uses a model relying on explanatory variables (for example, effect size varies with grade level) to explain the effect sizes for a whole set of studies, tests of model specification play a role analogous to that of the test of homogeneity. It is difficult to argue that additional variables are needed to explain the variation in effect sizes if the specification test suggests that additional variables are not needed.

Evidence that the model is correctly specified does not necessarily mean that the artifacts of design flaws can be ignored. If all studies share a common design flaw, then the results of all the studies may be biased to an unknown extent. If design flaws correlate with explanatory variables, then the effects of the design flaws are confounded with the effects of the explanatory variables. It may be difficult or impossible to determine the real source of the effect. However, if several design flaws are uncorrelated with the explanatory variables and if simple models appear to be specified correctly, then it does not seem plausible that inferences about effect sizes are artifacts of bias created by design flaws.

Problems in Obtaining Well-Specified Models

It may seem unlikely that the messy data generally obtained by social science research would be amenable to serious modeling of the type described in this chapter. Cynics may believe that model specification will always be rejected. However, my own experience in reanalyzing several meta-analyses suggests that the data from research studies in education and psychology are often consistent with relatively simple models.

Nevertheless, it is rare that an entire collection of effect sizes is homogeneous. Effect sizes calculated on different metrics—for example, raw posttest scores and analysis of covariance–adjusted posttest scores—are rarely consistent with one another. Variations in experimental procedure must sometimes be used as explanatory variables. Even when all studies measure a common dependent variable, such as conformity, different measurement procedures can cause effect size to vary. Perhaps the most significant explanatory variable is the degree of preexisting difference between the experimental and the control groups. Well-controlled studies—for example, those with small pretest differences or those using random assignment—often provide effect sizes that are homogeneous or that conform to simple models. Poorly controlled studies rarely conform to simple models. Even when the average effect size for well-controlled studies agrees with that of poorly controlled studies, effect sizes for the poorly controlled studies often exhibit much greater variability.

Appendix: Computing H_T, H_B, and H_W

Although equation 9 helps to illustrate the intuitive nature of the H_T statistic, a computational formula is more useful in computing actual H_T values. It can be shown that equation 9 is algebraically equivalent to the computational formula

(12) $$H_T = \sum_{i=1}^{k} w_i d_i^2 - (\sum_{i=1}^{k} w_i d_i)^2 / (\sum_{i=1}^{k} w_i)$$

The advantage of equation 12 is that H_T can be computed from the sums across studies of three variables: w_i, $w_i d_i$, and $w_i d_i^2$. The weighted mean d. and its variance v. can also be computed from sums of w_i and $w_i d_i$. Consequently, any packaged computer program that computes sums or means can be used to obtain the components of H_T, d., and v. in a single run.

The easiest way of computing the statistics needed for the analysis of variance of effect sizes is to compute three additional variables for each study: w_i, given in equation 7, $w_i d_i$, and $w_i d_i^2$. The sums of these three variables across all studies can be used with equation 12 to compute H_T. Obtaining the sums of w_i, $w_i d_i$, and $w_i d_i^2$ for each group of studies separately permits H_{Wi} to be computed for each group. Then, H_W is calculated as $H_X = H_{W1} + \ldots + H_{Wp}$. It is easiest to compute H_B as $H_B = H_T - H_W$. Note that the sums of w_i and $w_i d_i$ for each group of studies also permit the weighted mean effect size d_i. and its variance v_i. to be computed.

References

Eysenck, H. J. "An Exercise in Mega-Silliness." *American Psychologist,* 1978, *33,* 517.

Glass, G. V. "Primary, Secondary, and Meta-Analysis of Research." *Educational Researcher,* 1976, *5,* 3–8.

Glass, G. V., McGaw, B., and Smith, M. L. *Meta-Analysis in Social Research.* Beverly Hills, Calif.: Sage, 1981.

Glass, G. V., Peckham, P. D., and Sanders, J. R. "Consequences of Failure to Meet Assumptions Underlying the Fixed Effects Analyses of Variance and Covariance." *Review of Educational Research*, 1972, *42*, 237–288.

Glass, G. V., and Smith, M. L. "Meta-Analysis of Research on the Relationship of Class Size and Achievement." *Educational Evaluation and Policy Analysis*, 1979, *1*, 2–16.

Hedges, L. V. "Distribution Theory for Glass's Estimator of Effect Size and Related Estimators." *Journal of Educational Statistics*, 1981, *6*, 107–128.

Hedges, L. V. "Estimation of Effect Size from a Series of Independent Experiments." *Psychological Bulletin*, 1982a, *92*, 490–499.

Hedges, L. V. "Fitting Categorical Models to Effect Sizes from a Series of Experiments." *Journal of Educational Statistics*, 1982b, *7*, 119–137.

Hedges, L. V. "Fitting Continuous Models to Effect Size Data." *Journal of Educational Statistics*, 1982c, *7*, 245–270.

Presby, S. "Overly Broad Categories Obscure Important Differences Between Therapies." *American Psychologist*, 1978, *33*, 514–515.

Rosenthal, R., and Rubin, D. B. "Comparing Effect Sizes of Independent Studies." *Psychological Bulletin*, 1982, *92*, 500–504.

Smith, M. L., and Glass, G. V. "Meta-Analysis of Psychotherapy Outcome Studies." *American Psychologist*, 1977, *32*, 752–760.

Smith, M. L., and Glass, G. V. "Meta-Analysis of Class Size and Its Relationship to Attitudes and Instruction." *American Educational Research Journal*, 1980, *17*, 419–433.

Larry V. Hedges is assistant professor of education at the University of Chicago. His current research interests include statistical methods in educational research and evaluation and methodology for the quantitative synthesis of research.

The problems confronted in the synthesis of medical research are
relevant to systematic reviews in other substantive areas. This
chapter shows how some of these methodological problems can
be solved.

Evaluation Issues in Medical Research Synthesis

William H. Yeaton
Paul M. Wortman

The assessment of innovative medical technologies—for example, of surgeries, diagnostic procedures, and drugs—has considerable importance both for the nation (Fineberg and Hiatt, 1979; Office of Technology Assessment, 1976) and for the evaluation community (Wortman, 1981a). This importance is related both to the mounting cost of medical technologies and to concerns for their safety and effectiveness. In response to these concerns, Congress has taken several steps aimed at assessing new medical technologies, among them establishment of the Office of Technology Assessment (OTA), which is responsible for assessment of both medical and nonmedical technologies. That agency defines technology assessment as a "comprehensive form of policy research that examines the... social consequences... of technology" (OTA, 1976, p. 45). While technology assessment is concerned with a wide range of outcomes, it has concentrated on three issues—cost-effectiveness, safety, and effectiveness.

The effectiveness dimension of technology assessment is most likely to interest those who conduct research syntheses. In the same way that technology assessment considers multiple sets of evidence on a variety of outcomes, research synthesis seeks to integrate the findings of multiple studies dealing with a single outcome. The similar purpose makes the research synthesis approach readily applicable to technology assessment (OTA, 1982).

W. H. Yeaton, P. M. Wortman (Eds.). *Issues in Data Synthesis.*
New Directions for Program Evaluation, no. 24. San Francisco: Jossey-Bass, December 1984.

Other aspects of medical research make it particularly ripe for synthesis. Probably the most important aspect is the small benefit that is often associated with medical outcomes (Gilbert and others, 1977). Individual research studies yield results distributed on both sides of this small expected value and thus lead to conflicting claims of effectiveness, ineffectiveness, or harmfulness. However, aggregation of results across individual studies or patients can provide more stable estimates of treatment effects and enhance the statistical power to detect real differences among treatments.

A particularly compelling example of the use of research synthesis procedures to evaluate a medical technology has been provided by Baum and others (1981). In that study, the effectiveness of antibiotics was determined by comparing patients who received antibiotics prior to colorectal surgery with patients who did not. In twenty-six randomized clinical trials published between 1965 and 1980, these authors found that prophylactic use of antibiotics consistently helped to reduce the incidence of wound infections and mortality rates. By aggregating the results from individual studies, which typically used very small samples, the authors found that a clinically and statistically significant benefit favoring treatment could have been identified as early as 1969 after only five studies. Unfortunately, a synthesis of these results was not available to the medical community, and no-treatment controls continued to be used to assess the effectiveness of antibiotic use.

Chapter Five in this volume points out yet another important advantage of the research synthesis approach—its ability to produce a timely assessment of effectiveness in a policy context. This advantage is important for medical problems, because new medical technologies are often disseminated quite rapidly to practitioners without rigorous assessment of their effectiveness. Miao (1977) provides a particularly cogent example of this pattern. Timely synthesis of relevant research can stem premature dissemination by overly zealous medical practitioners, and it can provide the federal agencies responsible for making Medicaid and Medicare reimbursement decisions with improved estimates of effectiveness.

Medical technology assessment presents the research synthesizer with some special problems. In this chapter, we argue that the lessons learned in adapting the research synthesis approach to the study of medical technologies are relevant to the study of technologies in other substantive areas, particularly mental health (Yeaton, 1982). Thus, this chapter has four primary purposes: to describe the problems encountered in conducting research syntheses of medical studies, to suggest some solutions to these problems, to illustrate the solutions in the context of a research synthesis that we have conducted, and to elaborate the points in other substantive areas to which these solutions apply.

Evaluation in the Context of Change

Assessment of new medical technologies is particularly difficult since numerous features of the research context change over time (Wagner, 1979).

Moreover, each of these features is likely to affect outcomes. Chapter Two in this volume describes some procedures that can be used to determine whether there is systematic variation in the outcomes of primary studies. When variation is observed, it is important to pinpoint its source. The discussion that follows outlines some of the contextual changes that explain variation in outcomes over time and illustrates ways in which these changes can be related to outcomes.

Both the problems created for research synthesis by the context of change and solutions to these problems can be illustrated by our synthesis of results of coronary artery bypass graft surgery (Wortman and Yeaton, 1983). In this surgical procedure, a vein from the patient's leg is typically used to bypass one or more occluded coronary arteries, thereby increasing the flow of oxygenated blood to the heart. In the early 1970s, bypass graft surgery emerged as an important procedure for treatment of coronary heart disease, despite the absence of controlled trials demonstrating the benefits of such surgery. Recent estimates (Kolata, 1983) suggest that more than 150,000 patients receive such grafts in the U.S. every year at a cost of between \$2.5 and \$3 billion. The central question for research in this area is whether patients who receive this surgery are likely to live longer than patients who remain on a drug regimen.

Changes in the Surgical Technology. Coronary artery bypass graft surgery has changed considerably in the fifteen or so years since it was first introduced, as surgeons have gained experience with the procedure. In this respect, it resembles other new procedures in medicine and other fields that undergo a period of fine-tuning after adoption. However, this process of refinement presents problems for the analyst, as inferences made from the entire research literature may not be applicable to the current form of the operative procedure.

Inspection of the literature on bypass surgery reveals that two regularly reported aspects of the procedure have changed over time: the number of bypass grafts provided in each surgery and the patency of the graft (that is, the free flow of blood through the artery). Since both the number of grafts and the extent to which a graft allows oxygenated blood to reach the heart are critical to proper functioning, changes in both aspects are potentially linked to survival.

Solutions. These changes over a fifteen year period can be conceptualized as changes in the strength and integrity of the surgical treatment (Yeaton and Sechrest, 1981). Strength refers to the a priori probability that the treatment will have its intended effect. As such it is similar to the dosage levels of a drug. For coronary-artery surgery it should be reflected in the number of bypass grafts given during an operation. Integrity is the extent to which the treatment is actually administered as intended. Although the patency rate of grafts reflects other factors, such as the potential of existing arteries for repair and the length of follow-up, it should also be indicative of the proper implementation of a bypass graft.

Our strategy was to record both the number of grafts per operation and the patency rate and to relate these two variables to survival. We found a statistically significant increase in the number of grafts, from 2 in the 1970–1975 period to 2.3 in the 1976–1981 period (Yeaton and Wortman, 1983). Thus, any conclusions regarding survival have to be considered in the context of increasing treatment strength. At the same time, we found a slight and nonsignificant decrease in the patency rate from 81.9 percent in the 1970–1975 period to 80.3 percent in the 1976–1981 period. Thus, more occluded arteries were being bypassed without a sacrifice in the quality of the graft itself. Finally, we systematically noted the operative mortality rates reported in each study. While changes in operative mortality directly reflect the safety of the technology, it can be argued that they also reflect changes in treatment strength and integrity. The operative mortality was 6.2 percent in the 1970–1975 period and 3.8 percent in the 1976–1981 period, a statistically significant difference. Again, these data suggest that the technology has changed.

Implications for Other Technologies. In other substantive areas in which technology is expected to change over time, it seems equally important to record changes in the technology and to relate them to changes in primary outcomes. For example, psychotherapy has changed considerably since it first began to be used. Then, psychoanalysis was the dominant approach. Now, a wide variety of less time-consuming approaches is available. Certainly, changes in this mental health technology, for example, such factors as length of therapy sessions, number of sessions, the psychotherapist's training, and the use of purely analytic procedures, are likely to influence its ultimate effectiveness. In fact, the meta-analysis conducted by Smith and Glass (1977) found different effects for different types of therapy. Perhaps the claims of ineffectiveness leveled by psychotherapy's most vehement critics (for example, Eysenck, 1961) are not so much either right or wrong as they are outdated. If the psychotherapy implemented in the 1960s is not the psychotherapy that is being implemented in the 1980s, then data that seem to demonstrate the relative benefits of psychotherapy (Smith and others, 1980) may be confounded by changes in the technology over time.

Changes in the Mix of Patients Receiving Surgery. While the major question for bypass surgery is its effect on patient survival, an important related question concerns its benefits for patients with coronary disease of differing severity and type. Early results (Murphy and others, 1977) that were later confirmed (CASS, 1983) indicated that patients who had left main artery disease were more likely to survive than patients who remained on a drug regimen. (The left main artery supplies oxygenated blood to two of the heart's three coronary arteries.) Thus, early evidence strongly suggested that the prognosis for this subset of patients was likely to be positive.

This finding had the immediate effect of changing the relative mix of patients in controlled trials of coronary artery bypass graft surgery. Since it would be unethical to withhold a proven benefit from candidates for bypass graft surgery, left main artery patients were generally excluded from comparative studies. Thus, early studies had a larger percentage of left main artery patients than later studies did.

Solutions. The most obvious solution to this problem is to report mortality within patient types. This is the solution that we attempted. In the literature on bypass graft surgery, patients were typically categorized by the number of diseased vessels involved: one, two, and three or more. Unfortunately, it was not possible to include these data in our synthesis, since most of the original studies did not report them. However, we were able to record the percent of patients who suffered from one-, two-, or three-vessel disease, but not their mortality rates.

During the 1970–1976 period, the percentages of one- and two-vessel disease patients were higher (25.5 percent and 40.9 percent, respectively) than they were in the 1976–1981 period (19.2 percent and 35.5 percent, respectively). This pattern was reversed for three-vessel disease patients: The percentage of three-vessel disease patients was higher in the later studies (45.3 percent) than it was in the earlier studies (33.6 percent). Thus, the proportion of seriously diseased patients increased during the period in which this medical technology was assessed. Combining this finding with the others just cited, we concluded that more seriously diseased patients received a greater number of bypass grafts during the later period of study. Despite this trend, however, the patency rate did not decline, and operative mortality decreased during the twelve-year period covered by our synthesis.

The potential of the solution just described can be illustrated by the National Heart, Lung, and Blood Institute's Coronary Artery Surgery Study (CASS, 1983) recently completed at a total cost of $24 million (Kolata, 1983). This study sought to determine the advantages of coronary artery bypass graft surgery for patients suffering from mild heart disease. It found no difference in mortality between patients who received surgery and patients who were treated with drugs. A synthesis of the outcomes in the nine randomized clinical trials reported during this period could have shown benefits for mildly diseased patients if appropriate information had been made available in each study. Moreover, the synthesis results would have taken much less time and expense to produce, and its statistical power would have been greater owing to the large sample sizes being tested. As it was, the findings for patients suffering slightly more coronary artery disease were nearly identical to those obtained by CASS.

Implications for Other Technologies. Certainly, most service providers are interested in determining the characteristics of those most suited for treatment with a new technology. Moreover, it is possible that the particular mix of those with whom a new technology is used will change over time as professionals learn which types of persons respond favorably and unfavorably to the treatment. While it is not difficult to subtantiate the existence of subject-by-treatment interactions, as Chapters Two and Four in this volume show, a recent synthesis of the research on polygraph testing has noted that less attention appears to have been paid to the characteristics of subjects (Saxe and others, 1983). These authors note that most research studies omit such basic information as gender composition. Without such information, we run the risk of stating conclusions based on overall synthesis results that may not apply to everyone who receives treatment. To extend the polygraph testing example further, the mix of persons who are being tested today probably differs from the mix of those examined even ten years ago, given the current emphasis on personnel screening. Saxe and others (1983) found that this area had not been well researched, thus rendering comparisons across time invalid.

Changes in the Research Design. The type of research used to assess the effectiveness of coronary bypass graft surgery has changed considerably since the technology was introduced in the late 1960s. Early studies were entirely observational, and it was not until 1974 that the first controlled study was published (Wortman and Yeaton, 1983). Eight of the nine published randomized clinical trials appeared after 1977, and fourteen of the sixteen controlled trials that did not use randomization were published in the period between 1974 and 1978.

This pattern — poorly controlled early studies and well-controlled later studies — is consistent with the patterns found for other medical technologies, such as portacaval shunt and electronic fetal monitoring (Wortman, 1981b). In our synthesis of published studies assessing the effectiveness of coronary artery bypass graft surgery between 1970 and 1981 (Yeaton and Wortman, 1983), we examined the impact of design by noting the authors' interpretations of their results. The authors of the less well-controlled studies claimed greater benefits than the authors of the more well-controlled studies. Thus, the research design was confounded over time, and the enthusiasm raised by the technology's major outcome systematically decreased during this period.

Authors' interpretations of results were associated with the size of the treatment effect. Quasi-experiments that used some sort of matching strategy in an attempt to produce equivalent surgical and medical groups had a much larger mortality difference between the two groups than did studies that used a random procedure to assign patients. (The difference favored the surgical group for both kinds of studies.) This design effect was considerable — between 17 and 18 percent for quasi-experiments and between 4 and 5 percent for randomized clinical trials. Consistent with our finding that the quality of research had changed markedly during the period, we found a wide range in the size of the design effect over time.

Another design-related aspect that has changed considerably since the first studies of coronary artery bypass graft surgery is the makeup of the control group — the patients who remained on a medical regimen. The medication available to persons suffering from coronary heart disease has improved considerably in the last fifteen years. Empirical evidence strongly suggests that beta blockers are associated with beneficial quality-of-life and mortality results (Norwegian Multicenter Study Group, 1981), while the emergence of calcium blockers (Zelis, 1982) has added yet another potent medical force to the war against coronary heart disease. Thus, patients placed on a medical regimen in the later part of the fifteen-year assessment period would be more likely to survive than those who received the medical treatment in the earlier period. In addition, the national rate of mortality from coronary heart disease has declined substantially (Levy, 1981), which should also decrease the mortality rate among those in the medical group.

Solutions. Given both the existence of a design effect and its changing magnitude, we decided to aggregate results by design type and to report these results on a yearly basis. This procedure enabled us to make a direct comparison of results from randomized clinical trials and quasi-experiments at specific time periods.

To account for changes in the medical regimen as well as for changes in the surgical technology, we subtracted the mortality rate of those in the surgical group from the mortality rate of those in the medical group for each study in the synthesis. This difference, which is analogous to the difference between group means in meta-analysis, effectively controls for the changing medical and surgical technologies in the overall assessment period, since it pinpoints a comparison at a specific point in time. Next, we aggregated results within a particular study year cumulatively over time. Thus, we were able to examine the relative benefit of surgery through any particular year. Alternatively, we could have aggregated cumulatively starting at the most recent year for which results were available. The alternative procedure places less weight on earlier, possibly outmoded results. However, one advantage of cumulating forward in time is that the researcher can identify the first period in which surgery has a statistically significant benefit (Baum and others, 1981). In addition, it allows the synthesis to be blocked or stratified into different time periods corresponding to major changes in the technology.

Implications for Other Technologies. The quality of the designs used to assess new technologies is apt to show considerable variation. Our results suggest that design differences, especially as they change systematically across time, should be examined as a possible confounding factor in assessment of outcomes. For example, Sacks and others (1982) compared the results of randomized clinical trials with those of studies that used historical controls (that is, with studies in which patients who had already been treated were compared with those in prospectively collected treatment groups). Studies using historical controls systematically overestimated outcomes. Consistent with the pattern already noted, for five of the six therapies studied by Sacks and others, including coronary artery bypass graft surgery, the average year of publication was one to sixteen years in the randomized clinical trials. Thus early studies tend to use weaker designs that are more susceptible to bias.

Certainly, it is not difficult to locate design effects in fields other than medicine. One need look no further than Chapter One in this volume to find an example in education. In the research synthesis of outcomes in segregated and desegregated schools described there, outcomes were found to be generally more modest in relatively well-controlled studies. Even research by Glass, who has argued forcefully against selective aggregation of the results of better-controlled studies, suggests that design effects occur in education (Glass and Smith, 1979). In the study by Glass and Smith, achievement scores were higher in the better-controlled studies than they were in the relatively poorly designed studies, irrespective of class size, which indicates that poorer designs can lead to underestimates as well as to overestimates.

Aggregating Medical Dependent Variables

Medical research can be distinguished from social science research by the dependent variable in question. In is quite common for medical results to be reported as rates or proportions, such as the proportion of surgical patients who died during follow-up or the survival rate of medical patients after five years. Since the standard effect size measure entails taking a difference between the means of two groups and dividing by an appropriate standard deviation, analogous measures involving proportions are reasonable.

Solutions. The calculation of an effect size based on the difference between proportions is not complicated. In our synthesis of the research on coronary artery bypass graft surgery, we used the formula and tables provided by Cohen (1977) to calculate effect size for each study. The adjustments that Cohen provides resulted in difference scores nearly identical to those based on the raw difference in mortality between medical and surgical groups.

We were also familiar with the approach reported by Gilbert and others (1977), which uses the standard deviation of differences in calculating effect size. Since we were not aware of criteria that would argue strongly for these authors' method over Cohen's, we reported both, as well as the simple difference between proportions. Each method led to similar conclusions, which indicates that our major conclusions were not restricted to the method of analysis used.

Medical and biostatistical researchers have used still other methods for aggregating results unique to medical research. We will outline those methods here and refer interested readers to the references cited for detailed information. Stampfer and others (1982) pooled the results of randomized trials comparing the effect of intravenous streptokinase on acute myocardial infarction with the effects found in control groups. For these authors, the basic effect size measure was the risk ratio, which they defined as the proportion of deaths in the streptokinase-treated patients divided by the proportion of deaths among controls. Sheehe (1966) provides a detailed, step-by-step description of the computation of this relative risk statistic. With Sheehe's method, one can test for significance of the risk ratio within individual studies as well as for the aggregated risk ratio across studies. This method also allows confidence intervals to be calculated (Baptiste and Pike, 1977) both within and across studies so that overall patterns of effect size can be compared and tested statistically.

The methods developed by Mantel and Haenszel (1959) for analysis of survival data have been used to test for the effects of beta blockers on the incidence of myocardial infarction in randomized trials (Yusuf and others, 1983). Arguing that patients within studies cannot be assumed to be comparable, although chi square tests of heterogeneity conducted both by these authors and by Stampfer and others (1982) were nonsignificant, these authors first calculated the observed minus expected values and their variances within each study and then aggregated the resulting values across studies. Observed minus expected values, both within individual studies and aggregated across studies, can then be divided by the appropriate standard deviation for purposes of statistical testing.

As these examples show, in contrast to the standard effect size measures used in meta-analysis, a host of appropriate measures can be used to aggregate the outcomes likely to be found in medical studies. We hold no particular allegiance to any of these measures. The small number of syntheses conducted to date does not allow us to state any meaningful rules of thumb for choosing among them. Our approach has been to report more than one estimate in case of doubt about the best estimate and to compare results. Other researchers have used this strategy both in education (Wortman and others, 1978) and in economic research (Thompson, 1980), which has the advantage of demonstrating that findings are not analysis-specific.

Implications for Other Technologies. It seems very likely that research synthesizers who wish to embark on a new area of substantive inquiry will need to learn a new analysis procedure, as Chapter Two in this volume argues. One particularly telling instance of this likelihood is the recent work of Hunter and others (1982), who extended the data aggregation procedures of Glass and his colleagues to data sets reporting correlations.

Recently, the U.S. government became interested in developing and evaluating health and mental health intervention programs that emphasize prevention. The relationship between work stress and such mental health outcomes as alcohol and drug abuse has been the focus of particular interest (Price and others, 1980). Use of the data synthesis approach to quantify the relationship between stress and mental health problems would entail aggregation of correlations. The work by Hunter and others (1982) and illustrative applications of their methods by Mabe and West (1982) would be quite helpful in such synthesis. The results could be used to develop intervention programs.

Aggregating Studies with Consistent Flaws

A particularly thorny problem occurs when the primary studies all share the same weakness. Any research synthesis of these studies will yield a biased estimate of effect, which may be of indeterminate size. In this section, we discuss this dilemma in the context of a medical problem that has considerable relevance to a nonmedical audience.

Crossovers. To use standard evaluation terminology, the problem of crossovers is a specific case of differential attrition. Crossovers are particularly prevalent in randomized studies of coronary artery bypass graft surgery, because surgery has caused the percent of patients suffering from the disabling effects of angina to decline dramatically. Thus, patients assigned to medical regimens often insisted on a surgical option to relieve severe angina, and for ethical reasons physicians could not deny them its supposed benefit. From the methodologist's point of view, however, crossovers from the medical group who subsequently receive surgery cause formidable analytic headaches. Not only was the crossover rate substantial — approximately 20 percent — but the evidence also indicated that the crossovers were the medical patients with the worst prognosis (Murphy and others, 1977).

Solutions. To deal with the problem of crossovers, investigators have analyzed results in four different ways: by original treatment assignment; by treatment actually received; by treatment assigned, with all nonadherents removed; and by treatment assigned, with nonadherents considered lost to follow-up at the time of treatment change. The question that confronts the methodologist is this: Do any of these analysis procedures produce unbiased estimates of the effect of surgery? Unfortunately, the answer is no.

The solution that we have preferred is statistical in nature (Yeaton and others, 1983), so it depends on the appropriateness of the assumptions that must be made (for example, that only medical patients with the worst prognosis cross over or that the health status of medical patients is normally distributed). In principle, this solution relies on worst-case assumptions to determine the maximum degree of influence that can be attributed to crossovers. It resembles the sensitivity analysis used by economists in conducting cost-benefit and cost-effectiveness analyses under various assumed values for the discount rate. When conclusions are preserved regardless of the values assumed, the analyst can be relatively certain that the results are valid. When conclusions are contingent on the values assumed, the plausibility of the findings is a matter for judgment. Applying this solution to the synthesis of research on coronary artery bypass graft surgery, we judged that effects of crossovers could not account for enough of the difference between the surgical and medical groups to allow us to reject the beneficial effect of surgery.

Implications for Other Technologies. Special efforts are called for where primary studies share a common flaw. The consistent presence of crossovers restricts inference in any synthesis of research in which secondary outcomes are intrinsically desirable and in which their desirability results in pressure to relax adherence to the treatment protocol.

More generally, the synthesist has to use methodological foresight to anticipate shared flaws and develop practical solutions. For the authors of Chapter One in this volume, selection was a consistent and important threat to the internal validity of the studies that they were synthesizing. By coding for this threat and by conducting separate analyses, the authors were able to quantify the role of selection in outcomes. The initial selection differences were found to account for half of the effects obtained with traditional methods (Wortman and Bryant, forthcoming).

Benefits of Medical Research Synthesis

Medical research synthesis has considerable value for evaluations of other innovations. Examples from other areas, such as mental health, have been used in this chapter to illustrate the implications of solutions and important issues that are likely to be encountered in other fields. We hope that the discussion in this section of some common threads between medical technology and other areas will help evaluation researchers who wish to generalize synthesis procedures still further.

Of course, medical research synthesis has an intrinsic value that goes beyond its capacity to facilitate work in other domains. The medical literature offers unique opportunities for the investigation of many methodological matters. For example, most of the issues raised by the coronary artery bypass graft surgery synthesis can be discussed in terms of the four major threats to validity described by Cook and Campbell (1979), as Wortman (1983) has suggested and as Chapter One in this volume shows. The changing patient mix between the early and the late stages of coronary artery bypass graft surgery research poses a problem for external validity. Concurrent changes in the surgical procedure suggest that construct validity has been compromised. The problem of estimating effect size in quasi-experiments and systematically flawed randomized clinical trials, the changing nature of the medical control condition, and the complications introduced by crossovers all raise concerns for internal validity. And finally, the use of appropriate effect size estimates for dependent variables expressed as rates or proportions raises concerns for statistical conclusion validity.

Medical research synthesis also enables us to assess the role of randomization in medical research. Of course, we need a sufficient number of studies in order to compare effect sizes found in studies that assign patients to groups at random and in studies that do not. Perhaps because of the pressure to disseminate novel technologies before their worth has been proven, medical research makes such comparison possible, since many early studies do not use random assignment. In fact, we attempted in our research to quantify the contribution of research methodology — the so-called design effect — when estimating effect size.

Synthesis lends itself to the assessment of many methodological factors. The synthesis recently completed by Chalmers and his colleagues (Chalmers and others, 1983) provides a cogent example. The aim of that synthesis was to identify a mechanism that could account for a design effect. These investigators examined three kinds of studies: randomized blinded, randomized unblinded, and nonrandomized. In the blinded studies, random assignments to groups were made only after patients had been accepted into the study and their informed consent had been obtained. In the unblinded studies, patients were accepted or rejected for the study only after the physician was aware of their treatment assignment. This allowed any inherent bias in the physician to operate in selecting patients or in encouraging them to participate in the study. In the nonrandomized studies, assignments were nonrandom, and both concurrent and historical controls were allowed.

In the blinded randomized group of studies, 3.5 percent of the baseline measures between the treatment and control groups were significantly different. In the unblinded randomized studies, 7 percent of the measures were significantly different, and in the studies using nonrandom assignment, 34.4 percent were significantly different. Thus, the intent of randomization — to equate baseline values between the two groups being compared — was not fulfilled in the quasi-experiments or in the randomized studies in which physician bias could affect selection. When the results of the three types of studies were related to the distributions of prognostic variables, the lowest percent of statistically significant results and the smallest difference between treatment and control outcomes were found in the randomized blinded condition. Both values increased dramatically in the randomized unblinded and the nonrandomized conditions.

Thus, synthesis tends to focus the attention of the research community on the fundamental role of methodology in the assessment of medical technology. Early efforts have substantiated the importance of this new focus, as outlined in this chapter. However, careful planning and intimate knowledge of content are necessary in order to target and code for the methodological flaws common to primary studies. In particular, we have noted the prevalence of problems relating to temporal change, persons receiving treatment, research design, analytic procedures, and threats to validity. It is our hope that the solutions that we developed in assessing medical technologies will enhance the planfulness and methodological acumen of researchers in other substantive areas.

References

Baptiste, J., and Pike, M. C. "Exact Two-Sided Confidence Limits for the Odds Ratio in a Two-by-Two Table." *Applied Statistics,* 1977, *26,* 214–220.

Baum, M. L., Anish, D. S., Chalmers, T. C., Sacks, H. S., Smith, H., Jr., and Fagerstrom, R. M. "A Survey of Clinical Trials of Antibiotic Prophylaxis in Colon Surgery: Evidence Against Further Use of No-Treatment Controls." *New England Journal of Medicine,* 1981, *305,* 795–799.

Chalmers, T. C., Celano, P., Sacks, H. S., and Smith, H., Jr. "Bias in Treatment Assignment in Controlled Clinical Trials." *New England Journal of Medicine,* 1983, *309,* 1358–1361.

Cohen, J. *Statistical Power Analysis for the Behavioral Sciences.* New York: Academic Press, 1977.

Cook, T. D., and Campbell, D. T. *Quasi-Experimentation: Design and Analysis Issues for Field Settings.* Chicago: Rand McNally, 1979.

Coronary Artery Surgery Study Principal Investigators and Associates. "Coronary Artery Surgery Study (CASS): A Randomized Trial of Coronary Bypass Surgery; Survival Data." *Circulation,* 1983, *68,* 939–950.

Eysenck, H. F. "The Effects of Psychotherapy." In H. J. Eysenck (Ed.), *Handbook of Abnormal Psychology.* New York: Basic Books, 1961.

Fineberg, H. V., and Hiatt, H. H. "Evaluation of Medical Practices: The Case for Technology Assessment." *New England Journal of Medicine,* 1979, *301,* 1086–1091.

Gilbert, J. P., McPeek, B., and Mosteller, F. "Progress in Surgery and Anesthesia: Benefits and Risks of Innovative Therapy." In J. P. Bunker, B. A. Barnes, and F. Mosteller (Eds.), *Costs, Risks, and Benefits of Surgery.* New York: Oxford University Press, 1977.

Glass, G. V., and Smith, M. L. "Meta-Analysis of Research on the Relationship Class Size and Achievement." *Educational Evaluation and Policy Analysis,* 1979, *1,* 2–16.

Hunter, J. E., Schmidt, F. L., and Jackson, G. B. *Meta-Analysis: Cumulating Research Findings Across Studies.* Beverly Hills: Sage, 1982.

Kolata, G. "Some Bypass Surgery Unnecessary." *Science,* 1983, *222,* 605.

Levy, R. I. "Declining Mortality in Coronary Heart Disease." *Arteriosclerosis,* 1981, *1,* 312–325.

Mabe, P. A., III, and West, S. G. "Validity of Self-Evaluation of Ability: A Review and Meta-Analysis." *Journal of Applied Psychology,* 1982, *67,* 280–296.

Mantel, N., and Haenszel, W. "Statistical Aspects of the Analyses of Data from Retrospective Studies of Disease." *Journal of the National Cancer Institute,* 1959, *22,* 719–748.

Miao, L. L. "Gastric Freezing: An Example of the Evaluation of Medical Therapy by Randomized Clinical Trials." In J. P. Bunker, B. A. Barnes, and F. Mosteller (Eds.), *Costs, Risks, and Benefits of Surgery.* New York: Oxford University Press, 1977.

Murphy, M. L., Hultgren, H. N., Detre, K., Thomsen, J., and Takaro, T. "Special Correspondence: A Debate on Coronary Bypass." *New England Journal of Medicine,* 1977, *297,* 1470.

Murphy, M., Hultgren, H., Detre, K., Thomsen, J., Takaro, T., and Participants of the Veterans Administration Cooperative Study. "Treatment of Chronic Stable Angina: A Preliminary Report of Survival Data of the Randomized Veterans Administration Cooperative Study." *New England Journal of Medicine,* 1977, *297,* 621–627.

Norwegian Multicenter Study Group. "Timolol-Induced Reductions in Mortality and Reinfarction in Patients Surviving Acute Myocardial Infarction." *New England Journal of Medicine,* 1981, *304,* 801–807.

Office of Technology Assessment. *Development of Medical Technology: Opportunities for Assessment.* Washington, D.C.: U.S. Government Printing Office, 1976.

Office of Technology Assessment. *Strategies for Medical Technology Assessment.* Washington, D.C.: U.S. Government Printing Office, 1982.

Price, R. H., Ketterer, R. F., Bader, B. C., and Monahan, J. (Eds.). *Prevention in Community Mental Health: Research, Policy, and Practice.* Beverly Hills, Calif.: Sage, 1980.

Sacks, H., Chalmers, T. C., and Smith, H., Jr. "Randomized Versus Historical Controls for Clinical Trials." *American Journal of Medicine,* 1982, *72,* 233–240.

Saxe, L., Dougherty, D., and Cross, T. *Scientific Validity of Polygraph Testing: A Research Review and Evaluation.* Washington, D.C.: Office of Technology Assessment, 1983.

Sheehe, P. R. "Combination of Log-Relative Risk in Retrospective Studies of Disease." *American Journal of Public Health,* 1966, *56,* 1745–1750.

Smith, M. L., and Glass, G. V. "Meta-Analysis of Psychotherapy Outcome Studies." *American Psychologist,* 1977, *32,* 752–760.

Smith, M. L., Glass, G. V., and Miller, T. I. *Benefits of Psychotherapy.* Baltimore, Md.: Johns Hopkins University Press, 1980.

Stampfer, M. J., Goldhaber, S. Z., Yusuf, S., Peto, R., and Hennekens, C. H. "Effect of Intravenous Streptokinase on Acute Myocardial Infarction." *New England Journal of Medicine,* 1982, *307,* 1180–1182.

Thompson, M. S. *Benefit-Cost Analysis for Program Evaluation.* Beverly Hills, Calif.: Sage, 1980.

Wagner, J. L. *Toward a Research Agenda on Medical Technology.* DHEW Publication No. PHS 79-3254. Washington, D.C.: U.S. Government Printing Office, 1979.

Wortman, P. M. "Consensus Development." In P. M. Wortman (Ed.), *Methods for Evaluation Health Services.* Beverly Hills, Calif.: Sage, 1981a.

Wortman, P. M. "Randomized Clinical Trials." In P. M. Wortman (Ed.), *Methods for Evaluating Health Services.* Beverly Hills, Calif.: Sage, 1981b.

Wortman, P. M. "Evaluation Research: A Methodological Perspective." *Annual Review of Psychology,* 1983, *34,* 223–260.

Wortman, P. M., and Bryant, F. B. "School Desegregation and Black Student Achievement: An Integrative Review." *Sociological Methods of Research,* forthcoming.

Wortman, P. M., Reichardt, C. S., and St. Pierre, R. G. "The First Year of the Education Voucher Demonstration: A Secondary Analysis of Student Achievement Test Scores." *Evaluation Quarterly,* 1978, *2,* 193–214.

Wortman, P. M., and Yeaton, W. H. "Synthesis of Results in Controlled Trials of Coronary Artery Bypass Graft Surgery." In R. J. Light (Ed.), *Evaluation Studies Review Annual.* Vol. 8. Beverly Hills, Calif.: Sage, 1983.

Yeaton, W. H. "An Evaluation Research Perspective for Assessing New Psychotherapeutic Techniques." Paper presented at the 1982 meeting of the American Psychological Association, Washington, D.C., August 1982.

Yeaton, W. H., and Sechrest, L. "Critical Dimensions in the Choice and Maintenance of Successful Treatments: Strength, Integrity, and Effectiveness." *Journal of Consulting and Clinical Psychology,* 1981, *49,* 156–167.

Yeaton, W. H., and Wortman, P. M. "Medical Technology Assessment: The Evaluation of Coronary Artery Bypass Graft Surgery Using Data Synthesis Techniques." Unpublished manuscript, Institute for Social Research, Ann Arbor, Mich., 1983.

Yeaton, W. H., Wortman, P. M., and Langberg, N. "Differential Attrition: Estimating the Effect of Crossovers on the Evaluation of a Medical Technology." *Evaluation Review,* 1983, *7,* 831–840.

Yusuf, S., Peto, R., Lewis, J., and Sleight, P. "Beta Blockade During and After Myocardial Infarction: An Overview of the Randomized Trials." Unpublished manuscript, Clinical Trial Service Unit, Nuffield Department of Clinical Medicine, Radcliffe Infirmary, Oxford, England, 1983.

Zelis, R. "Calcium Blocker Therapy for Unstable Angina Pectoris." *New England Journal of Medicine,* 1982, *306,* 926–928.

William H. Yeaton is assistant research scientist at the Institute for Social Research at the University of Michigan. His current research interests include medical research methodology and research synthesis.

Paul M. Wortman is director of the Methodology and Evaluation Research Program in the Institute for Social Research and professor in the School of Public Health at the University of Michigan–Ann Arbor. His current research interests include research synthesis methods and medical technology assessment.

*Syntheses of research studies identify important interactions
that any one study rarely finds.*

Six Evaluation Issues That Synthesis Can Resolve Better Than Single Studies

Richard J. Light

What can a synthesis of evaluation studies do that a single study cannot? In this chapter, I will discuss six issues that synthesis helps us to resolve. The most frequently cited virtue of synthesis is that the increased sample size can increase statistical power. This virtue has been discussed widely (Glass, 1977; Glass and others, 1981; Hunter and others, 1982; Light and Smith, 1971). The six properties of synthesis that I want to emphasize here have little to do with sample size. What they have in common is that they help us to say *when* a social, medical, or educational program works, not just whether or not it works on the average.

One way we can identify when a program works is by focusing on inter-action. What do I mean by *interaction?* Statisticians often use this word to indicate nonlinearity. That is how I interpret the word here. In a program evaluation context, we can ask two questions: First, does the program work well for certain kinds of people and less well for others? Second, does the program work well in certain settings and less well in others? Both these questions are about interactions. A single study can find certain kinds of interactions, but synthesis of several studies can turn up much richer, more useful information.

This chapter was facilitated by a grant from the Alfred P. Sloane Foundation.

W. H. Yeaton, P. M. Wortman (Eds.). *Issues in Data Synthesis.*
New Directions for Program Evaluation, no. 24. San Francisco: Jossey-Bass, December 1984.

Why Are Interaction Effects Important?

Usually, social, educational, and health programs are evaluated to see how well they work. Good evaluations also examine how changes in program format could incrementally help to improve them. One way of asking whether a program works is to ask whether it works *on the average*. Another way is to ask whether it works for a subgroup of people or in special settings.

For policy purposes, the interaction question can be as important as the main effects question. For example, when a physician considers what anesthesia to give a patient prior to surgery and has a choice between two drugs, it is useful to learn which of the two is better on the average. However, it is even more valuable to learn which of the two is preferable for the precise surgery the patient will have. Or which of the two has a better track record for the particular kind of patient, such as a young male in excellent health. It would not be surprising to find, for example, that the anesthesia best suited for a twenty-year-old in excellent general health is different from the anesthesia best suited for a seventy-year-old in poor health.

Finding such interactions is important not only when making decisions for individuals but also when assessing the effectiveness of large-scale programs. Suppose that Head Start works generally well for children under four but far less well for children five years or older. That would be worth knowing. If resources for the program were limited, such knowledge could tell us where to concentrate them. Or, if substantial resources were available, this interaction finding would suggest that the Head Start curriculum should be modified for older children. So, whether the main purpose of an evaluation is to target resources or to change a program incrementally, finding an interaction can guide decisions.

Why Is Synthesis So Useful in Identifying Interactions?

Let us recall how a single research study can identify an interaction effect. Basically, there are two ways. One way is to build a search for the interaction directly into the study design. For example, let us hypothesize that job training program A works better for high school dropouts than it does for high school graduates and that the reverse is true for training program B. Then, if we have control over treatment assignments, we can test this hypothesis by making sure that all four combinations of people and program type are represented. Ideally, randomization will be used to develop the four groups—dropouts given A, dropouts given B, graduates given A, and graduates given B. Then, comparisons of the four effect sizes will give a clear indication of what program type works best, on the average, for what type of person. These findings will either refute or strengthen the initial hypothesis.

The other way of identifying interaction effects in a single study involves the use of post hoc procedures. Suppose that a search for interaction has not been formally designed into a study. In that case, such procedures as regression analysis and other applications of the general linear model can be applied retrospectively. The dilemmas and caveats involved in this process are well known (Anderson and others, 1980). If people were free to choose their own treatment, there may be self-selection. There may be confounding of background variables. For example, most of the high school dropouts may come from poor families in cities, while most of the graduates may come from middle-income families in rural areas. Suppose that a single study of this type did not assign people to training programs at random. Then, because the study was not designed to examine interaction, its findings could well be confounded by graduation status, setting, and family type.

Against this background, we can now address the central theme of this chapter—that research synthesis can be far more effective in identifying interactions than any single study. (For a discussion of the statistical procedure for detecting interactions, see Chapter Two in this volume.) Any one study is conducted in a particular context, under a particular set of constraints. Unless the study is extraordinarily large in scope, it has a limited group of participants who are assigned to treatments in a certain way. Each of these facts is good for a single study. It is important to know exactly what population is in and what population is out. It is important to know how people chose, or were assigned to, a treatment.

The advantage of looking at a group of evaluation studies is that the individual studies often take place in different contexts. And, we can learn much about interactions from noticing how findings relate to context. To illustrate this idea concretely, we can now address the six evaluation issues that synthesis can resolve better than any single study.

Synthesis Can Help to Match Treatment Type with Recipient Type

The Head Start program was created in the early 1960s in response to a growing belief that something had to be done to help poor children start school on a stronger footing. In 1964, Sargent Shriver, director of the Office of Economic Opportunity (OEO), formed a committee chaired by the pediatrician Robert Cooke. Its charge was to develop a program for reducing the effects of poverty on children. These efforts led to the creation of Head Start, which had seven concrete goals, including improving the child's mental processes and skills, with particular attention to conceptual and verbal skills.

The program was formally authorized to begin in summer 1965. Between 50,000 and 100,000 children were expected to participate in the first summer program. In fact, 560,000 did. By 1967, Head Start funding had grown to $349 million. OEO decided to evaluate its performance and contracted in 1968 with Westinghouse Learning Corporation and Ohio State University to conduct a formal evaluation. The findings were released in 1969, and they stunned the education community.

The key sentence in the Westinghouse final report (Cicirelli, 1969, p. 43) says: "Although this study indicates that full-year Head Start appears to be a more effective compensatory program than summer Head Start, its benefits cannot be described as satisfactory." According to Datta (1976, p. 134), "children who participated in Head Start summer programs did not score higher at the beginning of first, second, and third grades in such programs on all measures of academic achievement, linguistic development, and personal/social development than children who had not participated. Children who had attended the full-year programs and were tested in the first grade achieved higher scores on the Metropolitan Reading Test and some subtests of the Illinois Test of Psycholinguistic Abilities. Scores of children who had attended full-year programs and were tested in the second and third grade were not different from the scores of comparison children."

The disappointing findings of this evaluation generated great controversy. Smith and Bissell (1970), Campbell and Erlebacher (1970), and others criticized the methodology severely. Supporters of preschool education found many problems with the study's design and implementation. Yet, despite the criticism, the study had a large impact on policy. Supporters of Head Start were placed on the defensive. For example, both Alice Rivlin and Christopher Jencks, who supported such remedial programs as Head Start in the late 1960s, became more cautious after the Westinghouse-Ohio study. Rivlin (1971, p. 32) notes that "Jencks and his associates dismiss the whole preschool child development movement in a few skeptical paragraphs, citing the Westinghouse-Ohio study's findings that, on the average, Head Start children showed no long-term cognitive gains over non–Head Start children" (Datta, 1983).

How should we interpret the findings of this single, large study, which had such a large impact? A synthesis of early education programs conducted by Bissell (1970) throws much light on Head Start and related preschool programs. Her review emphasizes a search for interactions. Bissell reanalyzes data collected by three researchers: Karnes in Urbana, Illinois; DiLorenzo in New York state; and Weikart in Ypsilanti, Michigan. She chooses these three data sets because each author compared two or more specific curricula, each project had well-formulated goals, and each project was conducted and documented carefully.

Taken together, these three data sets compare five types of curriculum, each of which has supporters in the preschool community: the Karnes Ameliorative curriculum, a highly structured cognitive curriculum; the Bereiter-Engelmann curriculum, a highly structured informational program; a traditional enrichment program emphasizing language development, with a relatively permissive low-structure environment; a traditional enrichment program emphasizing psychosocial development, with a relatively permissive low-structure environment; and a Montessori program with a structured environment.

Bissell finds small main effects. For example, programs with strong quality control, well-trained staff, a high degree of staff supervision, and a low pupil-to-teacher ratio produce bigger cognitive gains than other programs. Her big finding involves interaction. To quote her (Bissell, 1970, p. 62): "Directive, highly structured preschool programs tend to be more effective with the *more* disadvantaged of poor children.... In contrast, nondirective, less-structured programs tend to be more effective with the *less* disadvantaged of poor children."

Bissell's data make her point sharply. The reanalyses of scores on three standardized tests—the Binet, the Peabody Picture Vocabulary Test, and the Illinois Test of Psycholinguistic Abilities—show that when a child is well matched with the optimal program (for example, exceptionally down-and-out children and highly structured programs), the average difference between experimental and control groups is between two thirds and three quarters of a standard deviation. If the match is poor (as when down-and-out children from poor backgrounds are exposed to a relatively open curriculum), the comparative gains are minimal. A few of the comparisons even find a marginally negative program effect.

A synthesis such as Bissell's has at least three virtues. First, since the individual evaluations examined projects organized to serve different children in different places with different programs, we get a broad panorama of findings. Second, since the data collected by several independent investigators display similar interaction patterns—that highly structured programs are better for the poorest children—the credibility of this overall finding is enhanced. Third, the synthesis of several evaluations puts the results of the single, big Westinghouse study in a new light. Most of the early Head Start sites, such as those examined by Westinghouse, had clearly open and permissive styles. They offered relatively little formal cognitive work. To quote Bissell (1970, p. 81), "directors favor supportive, unstructured, socialization programs rather than structured informational programs for poor children." Knowing this about the early Head Start centers that Westinghouse and Ohio State University examined and combining this fact with Bissell's review findings, we can see why the study found little success. There is also reason for optimism that student performance should improve as more structure is introduced at local Head Start sites.

Synthesis Can Explain Which Features of a Treatment Matter

In 1968, Rosenthal and Jacobson wrote: "As teaching training institutions begin to teach the possibility that teachers' expectations of their pupils' performance may serve as self-fulfilling prophecies, there may be new expectancy created. The new expectancy may be that children can learn more than had been believed possible, an expectation held by many educational theorists, though for quite different reasons" (p. 141).

Three years later, Baker and Crist (1971, p. 56) asserted the opposite:

"Teacher expectancy probably does not affect pupil IQ. This conclusion is supported by a background of decades of research suggesting the stability of human intelligence and its resistance to alterations by environmental manipulation, by the reanalysis of the Rosenthal and Jacobson (1968) study . . ., and by the failure of all replication studies to demonstrate effects on IQ."

So, here we find arguments from distinguished scholars that disagree sharply. The expectancy hypothesis is central to classroom conduct in education, because it has both substantive and ideological components. Suppose that teachers' expectations for a particular student's performance actually play a role in determining the student's performance. Some people see schools as perpetuating or even exacerbating inequality among children's life achievement. For these people, the expectancy argument offers a strong explanation for why poor children do less well in school than other children. Educators have vigorously debated the importance of teachers' expectations. Ryan (1971) and Kohl (1971) both argue that teachers expect less from poor children and therefore receive less. Elashoff and Snow (1971) argue the reverse — that methodological flaws in the study by Rosenthal and Jacobson (1968) undercut their findings.

To assess the importance of teacher expectancy on student IQs, Raudenbush (forthcoming) synthesized eighteen such experimental studies. Seventeen of these studies had a strong research design, in which children were assigned at random to treatments. While the eighteen studies include children of different ages and income groups, they all used IQ as an outcome measure. Raudenbush uses several different methods for combining studies in a quantitative meta-analysis (Fisher, 1973; Edgington, 1972; Winer, 1971; Mosteller and Bush, 1954). He emphasizes the effort to explain variation among outcomes (Pillemer and Light, 1980). His conclusion is not at all obvious for someone simply looking at the findings of eighteen studies: "The effect sizes of the studies, in standard deviation units, range from .55 down to − .13. Five of the eighteen achieved statistical significance, three at the .05 level and two at the .01 level. For the thirteen other studies, in five the experimental children scored higher than the controls, while in the other eight the control children scored higher" (Raudenbush, forthcoming).

Raudenbush's findings are clear and important. He finds a small average effect size across the eighteen studies of .11. But, as he reports, this main effect summary "certainly conceals more than it clarifies." That is because the studies can be divided into two broad groups. In one group, teachers were given information about each student (the "treatment") *after* a few weeks of initial contact. In the other group, teachers got information *before* they met students.

This difference between the two subgroups proved to be the key finding. Teachers who obtain information before they meet students show a strong expectancy effect. Teachers who obtain information after knowing students for several weeks show essentially no expectancy effect. To quantify this difference, the correlation between timing of the treatment induction and outcomes is $r = .68$. Raudenbush summarizes: "When no teacher-student contact preceded the experiment, the average probability level was .06. After the second week of teacher-student contact, only one reported a probability of less than .50."

So, this synthesis sheds light on a controversy that has raged for fifteen years. All these years, the debate focused on main effects: Does expectancy have a big effect or not? There seems to be a main effect, but it is very small. The synthesis tells us that the important treatment component lies in when the induction is given. It would be impossible to learn this from any one of the eighteen studies alone. In fact, one major finding of this synthesis is the consistency of treatment effect in studies where there was no prior teacher-student contact. Similarly, outcomes of studies where expectancy induction took place two weeks or more into the school year show very little variance. Raudenbush found that the big news in these studies is that when the treatment is implemented matters a lot. Knowing this enables us to understand how teacher expectancy works.

Synthesis Can Explain Conflicting Results

In the late 1970s, discussions of job training emphasized the importance of "integrated services." Evaluations of the Comprehensive Employment and Training Act, the broad umbrella jobs program budgeted at several billion dollars a year, were finding marginal success at best. Some of these evaluations (National Academy of Sciences, 1978, 1979) suggested that job training alone, when narrowly defined, could not break a family's cycle of poverty and unemployment. These assessments found that integrated services, which included matching a family's needs for education, health services, and job training with a well-coordinated group of "helpers," offered far more promise than a stand-alone jobs program.

To assess this idea, the U.S. Department of Labor initiated several studies of integrated services programs. The key idea was to coordinate a series of services for poor families in which job training was an important component but not the only component. Several demonstration programs took place at several different sites. Yet, the results were conflicting. While these conflicting findings about the value of integrated services were discouraging, the investigators ultimately capitalized on the varying outcomes to learn a great deal about the contexts in which integrated services worked well and worked badly and about how to organize a good matching plan between services and recipients.

The broad question, then, is, How can a synthesis harness different findings from several studies to enhance our understanding about a program's effectiveness? It is not rare in an effort to pull together information about a program's effects across studies to find that the studies provide severely conflicting information. These conflicts can be frustrating. Yet, it is precisely such conflicts that may give evaluators some insights into the matching problem. The job training example shows this. Let us look at some data, rounded off for illustrative purposes. Weeks of employment are the outcome measure.

Take the case of two studies conducted in different states by different investigators. Each compares an integrated service program with a single-service job training program. The study in one state looks at eighty men. Forty receive one program and forty receive the other. This study finds that the integrated services group has an average of eighty weeks of employment, while the single-service group has seventy weeks. Integrated services seem to be more effective. Yet, the study in the other state finds precisely the opposite. It also examines eighty men. Again, forty receive one program, and forty receive the other. Yet, this second study finds that the integrated services men work only sixty weeks, while the single-service men in the comparison group work an average of seventy weeks.

The results conflict. This is not unusual for evaluation studies, but it is frustrating. What can be done? An effort can be made to see if we can discover from this conflict something about matching people's needs to the services that are offered in an integrated plan. Here is how synthesis could explain the conflict: Categorize the eighty men in each study by their "problem" constellation. Such categorization can be difficult when the people or families served have multiple problems, but let us simplify here and assume that there are two broad types of problem sets, problem set A and problem set B. First, look at the *allocation* of people with each type of problem to each program in the two studies, then separate that allocation from the average *effect* found for those people in each program. Table 1 displays some results. The numbers in the cells are the effects—the average number of weeks employed for the men in each cell. The numbers between parentheses are the allocations—the number of men in that cell.

We can learn surprisingly much from this simple table. We see that although the grand means of the two studies caused the results to conflict, the two studies had identical effects for the groups of men receiving each treatment. Both studies found that men with problem set A who received integrated services were employed an average of ninety weeks, while men with problem

Table 1. Comparing Studies with Conflicting Outcomes

	Problem Set A	Problem Set B	Overall Means
Study One			
Integrated Services	90 (30)	50 (10)	80 (40)
Single Service	50 (20)	90 (20)	70 (40)
Study Two			
Integrated Services	90 (10)	50 (30)	60 (40)
Single Service	50 (20)	90 (20)	70 (40)

Source: Light, 1979.

set A who received the single service worked an average of only fifty weeks. And, both studies found that the reverse was true for men with problem set B. Why, then, was there a conflict? The conflict was caused by different allocations of problem types across the two service types in the two studies. In the first study, more A men than B men received integrated services. In the second study, the reverse was true. This difference in allocations, combined with the consistent finding of both studies that integrated services were more effective for men with problem set A and less effective for men with problem set B, created the conflict.

What policy implications can be drawn from this synthesis? If these data are in fact a good description of reality, we learn how integrated services should be targeted to a subgroup of people whose needs best match those services. And, the inkling that this might be the case emerged from an observation that two studies comparing integrated with single services reached opposite findings. It would not have emerged from either of the studies alone. We learn here that by examining program effects and allocations of people across studies, we can improve the matching process and target integrated services to those who will benefit the most.

Synthesis Can Determine Whether Relative or Absolute Performance Is the Critical Outcome

Most programs can be looked at in two different ways. One way is to see whether an intervention has taken hold as intended. For example, does the child really know how to count better? Does the drug for hypertension actually lower the patient's blood pressure? Is the prisoner who is about to be released actually a competent carpenter? The other way of assessing a program is to see what happens in the end. Does the child who now counts better get higher marks in school? Do the patients who now have lower blood pressure also have a lower incidence of heart attacks? Does the newly released carpenter earn a reasonable income with his new skills?

A synthesis of evaluation findings that is well done usually looks at the studies that it examines in both ways. But, it is worth noticing that synthesis has a special comparative advantage over any single study in answering the second question. This is because, while some programs can confer benefits or inculcate skills that indeed take hold, it is not always the case that these skills or benefits can be translated into concrete positive outcomes in the end. In particular, some benefits are valuable only in a comparative sense, because of the limited number of opportunities in which certain skills are useful. If too many others have the same skills, they become less valuable to any particular person who has them.

Job training can illustrate both points—the point about the comparative benefits and the point about the special value of synthesis. Suppose that a job skills program undertaken in one city is evaluated. The research design is excellent. One hundred applicants are divided at random into two groups. One group receives training to become carpenters, while the other group does not. If this evaluation finds that two years after the job program the trainees clearly earn more than the control group, what can we conclude? We would probably conclude that the job training works—and well we should, since the one available study has positive findings, and they come from a randomized experimental design allowing causal inferences.

Let us assume that this positive finding is noticed and that the same program is offered at ten other sites around the country. Learning from the excellent example set in the initial evaluation, each of the ten new sites organizes its own randomized trial. The results become available two years later, and they are difficult to interpret: At three sites, the training is a clear success; the trainees have good jobs. At two sites, it is at best marginal; only some trainees have jobs. At the other five sites, it didn't work at all.

Efforts to organize these ten findings into an evaluation synthesis can move forward in two quite different ways. One way is to emphasize the skills question—did the trainees at all ten sites become reasonably good carpenters? The other way is to emphasize the outcome question—why did the findings differ so much across the ten sites? By tackling both questions, synthesis can generate valuable insights. For example, a finding that sites varied enormously in their trainees' knowledge of carpentry provides management information. Clearly, the substantive training component needs to be improved across sites, and it needs to be strengthened in certain weak places. However, a finding that trainees learned carpentry quite well at all ten sites would be even more informative, because it would force us to ask why trainees differed so substantially across the ten sites in their ability to get jobs.

One possible explanation is that the benefit of the carpentry training for any one recipient depends on the number of other people who receive the training. Synthesis could support this explanation by examining the correlation across sites between the fraction of trainees who got jobs and the opportunity for success as measured by, say, the total population at each site. If the correlation is clearly positive, we learn three things. First, we learn that training works in a predictable way. Trainees in bigger cities have better prospects than trainees in smaller towns. Second, we learn two important things about the training itself—that it indeed confers skills on participants and that when relative performance is not a constraint on any one trainee—that is, when the trainee lives in a big city—the program succeeds. Third, we learn how to organize and manage such training programs better in the future: They are best targeted to settings in which there are opportunities for trainees to put their training to use.

To summarize, synthesis can identify programs whose value depends not only on their substantive features but also on the number of people who participate. That is, synthesis can point out when programs are constrained by limited opportunities for success. A single study cannot answer these questions.

Synthesis Can Assess the Stability of Treatment Effectiveness

Usually, any single study is organized by a single investigator or a small group of investigators, and it takes place in one or a very few sites. A single study at a single site allows us to assess whether a treatment worked. A single study at several sites allows us to assess whether the treatment worked overall. We can even examine the variance among outcomes at the several sites. But we cannot tell how robust the treatment is when it is provided by several different investigators or organizations. Only a synthesis of results across several studies allows us to answer this question. When each of several organizations implements the same program in different places, the variation in outcomes offers a good signal of the program's robustness. If it works extraordinarily well in a few places and poorly in others, we must try to explain why. But, whatever the explanation, we will have discovered that the program is not robust. We learn that it is sometimes effective but that its strength is easy to undercut. At some sites, the poor performance may be explained by weak implementation or by a poor match between recipients and program. The only way to assess the stability of a program in different settings is to see how it functions in different settings.

Special Supplemental Program for Women, Infants, and Children, known as the WIC program, illustrates these points. The U.S. Senate Committee on Agriculture, Nutrition, and Forestry asked the U.S. General Accounting Office (GAO) to synthesize all available evidence about WIC (U.S. GAO, 1984; Chapter Five in this volume provides detailed information about synthesis at the GAO). This program, funded at over $1.1 billion a year, provides nutrition supplements to approximately three million people each year. These people are pregnant women from low-income families and children from birth to age five in low-income families who are considered at high nutritional risk. The Senate Committee's request to the GAO was motivated by the sharply conflicting testimony that it received about WIC's effectiveness. Some witnesses argued that it was a highly effective program and that it had clear positive effects in increasing children's birthweight, reducing fetal and neonatal mortality, improving nutrition in mothers and children, and reducing mental retardation in children. Other witnesses argued that there was no concrete evidence for these positive assertions. They testified that while it seemed hardhearted to oppose the distribution of food vouchers to low-income mothers, the facts did not support assertions that women or their children benefited in any concrete way.

To resolve these conflicting claims, the GAO identified sixty-one evaluations of the WIC program. Using both internal staff and outside advisers, the agency asked several readers to examine each study independently and rate it for methodological quality. The findings about WIC's effect on birthweights illustrate how such a synthesis can provide useful information about the robustness of a given program. Only six of the sixty-one studies of WIC's overall effectiveness were rated by GAO and its advisers as reasonably high in quality. These six were then carefully examined for specific data about birth-weights. Table 2 presents these data.

It seems clear from Table 2 that both sides in the debate about WIC's effectiveness are overstating their case. Those who argue that WIC has major positive effects on birthweight are not supported by the empirical evidence. Among the six studies, the single most positive finding is a 3.9 percent increase in average birthweight. Yet, the case of those who argue that there is no concrete evidence for WIC's effectiveness is also weakened by this synthesis, because five of the six studies showed gains in birthweight, although the gains were small. The one study that showed a small loss in birthweight is based on a tiny sample — thirty-seven WIC participants and forty-two comparison children — while in the five other studies samples numbered in the several hundreds or several thousands. Moreover, the outlier is not statistically significant.

This GAO summary is instructive, because it tells us a lot about the impact that WIC is having on birthweights among participants. First, it is clear that the impact is never very great — a gain of perhaps 2 percent. Second, the small gain seems reasonably consistent, as the GAO (1984, p. 15) concluded: "On the average, there appears to be a positive benefit from WIC participation; a reasonable estimate is that the average birthweight of WIC infants is higher by somewhere between thirty and fifty grams." The robustness of this finding would not have been apparent from any single study — it took a review of six studies to identify the reasonably consistent, if small, effect.

Synthesis Can Assess the Importance of Research Design

Some scholars spend a large fraction of their time arguing that research design matters. Riecken and others (1974), Gilbert and others (1975), Chalmers (1982), and Hoaglin and others (1982) have worked hard to convince the evaluation community that randomization is a crucial ingredient for evaluations, since it underlies our ability to make causal inferences. The efforts of these investigators have made some headway. Yet, sometimes randomization is difficult or impossible, so we must turn to alternatives and do the best that we can despite their imperfections. Alternatives include case studies, quasi-experiments, observational designs, studies of management records, and computer simulations when appropriate (Hoaglin and others, 1982).

None of this is news. But, when a researcher or policy maker faces a concrete problem, such as whether a certain nutrition program is effective or whether a new surgical procedure is worth using, any single study is almost certain to have a single research design. There are a few exceptions, but they are rare (Ruopp and others, 1979). The reader of this one study must then ask two questions: First, does the study stand well on its own merit — is it well done? Second, does the research design introduce any constraints, limitations, or biases? It is difficult to answer this second question with evidence from only

Table 2. Mean Birthweight Quantitative Summary

| Study | Year and Location | Reported Birthweight (grams)[a] | | | Quantitative Indicators | | |
		WIC	Non-WIC	Raw Difference	Percent Difference[b]	Statistical Significance
Kotelchuck	1978 Massachusetts	3,281 (4,126)	3,260 (4,126)	21.0	0.6	Marginal
Metcoff	1980–82 Oklahoma City	3,254 (238)	3,163 (172)	91.0[c]	2.9	Yes
Stockbauer	1979–81 Missouri	3,254 (6,657)	3,238 (6,657)	16.0	0.5	Yes
Silverman	1971–77 Allegheny County, Pennsylvania	3,189 (1,047)	3,095 (1,361)	94.0	3.0	Yes
Bailey	1980 Two Florida counties	3,229 (37)	3,276 (42)	−47.0	−1.4	No
Kennedy	1973–78 Massachusetts	3,261.4	3,138.9	122.5	3.9	Yes
Summary						
Average		3,244.7	3,195.1	49.6	1.55[d]	
Weighted Average[e]		3,257.8	3,225.9	31.3	0.97[d]	
Range: Lowest		3,189.0	3,095.0	−47.0	−1.4	
Range: Highest		3,281.0	3,276.0	122.5	3.9	

[a] The numbers in parentheses are sample sizes.
[b] Raw difference divided by non-WIC birthweight.
[c] Adjusted.
[d] Average raw difference divided by average non-WIC birthweight.
[e] Each mean is weighted by the number of participants or controls in its group, and an overall average is obtained by dividing by the total number of participants and controls in the six studies. The raw difference is based on the total number of participants and controls.
Source: GAO 1984, p. 16.

one study, even one that is well done. But, a synthesis helps us a lot. It allows us to compare findings — and the research designs that lead to those findings — across a group of studies. Chapter Three in this volume provides a useful example. If there are correlations, we learn two things: First, we see what specific designs led to what specific outcomes. Second, we can organize future research knowing more about the consequences of specific designs.

Several concrete illustrations from recent syntheses show how research design can matter. One example comes from surgery. Chalmers (1982) reviews the findings from ninety-five studies of portacaval shunt surgery. These ninety-five reports were published over a period of many years by different investigators who worked at different hospitals. Chalmers asks two questions about each study: First, did its research design have adequate controls, poor controls, or no controls at all? Second, what did the investigator say about the surgery; was there marked enthusiasm, moderate enthusiasm, or no enthusiasm? The results of Chalmers's review are presented in Table 3. The conclusion here is clear: Poorly controlled studies of this surgery are far more likely than well-controlled studies to make investigators happy. Perhaps Table 3 illustrates Hugo Muench's law of clinical studies: Results can always be improved by omitting controls (Bearman and others, 1974).

A second example comes from the dilemma of how best to control spiraling health care costs. In 1982, the Committee on Labor and Human Resources of the U.S. Senate asked the General Accounting Office to examine all available evidence about the effects on medical costs of increasing the amount of health care provided at home for elderly citizens (U.S. GAO, 1982). It was proposed in Senate debate that by providing more health care at home, total service costs would drop, because the chronically ill would make less use of hospitals. To assess the cost implications of increased home care, the GAO reviewed more than thirty studies. About half were nonquantitative case studies, while the other half were comparative and used either an experimentally developed control group or an existing comparison group. The GAO's findings were striking. The case studies, mostly small-sample narrative reports, almost unanimously suggested that costs would decline. But, the quantitative studies found the opposite — that total costs would not decline; indeed, they might even increase slightly. The quantitative studies turned up

Table 3. Synthesis of Evidence on Portacaval Shunt Surgery

| Controls | Degree of Enthusiasm | | | Totals |
	Marked	Moderate	None	
Adequate	0	3	4	7
Poor	8	2	1	21
None	50	14	3	67
Totals	68	19	8	95

Source: Chalmers, 1982.

a clear reason for this surprising result. Rather than leading some elderly recipients of service to change the site from hospital to home, the new opportunity for home care considerably expanded the total number of people requesting care. People not receiving services began to request them. So, while the offering of reimbursable home care as an alternative to hospitalization can reduce the cost per recipient for those who accept the alternative, it seems also to create a substantial new group of service recipients, and total service costs do not drop.

I do not include this example to argue for or against home care. Some people argue that the home care option is a good idea even if costs are higher. Others disagree. But whatever one's values about the trade-offs between hospital and home care, the point is that a study's design is closely related to its outcome. A reviewer could examine every published case study and conclude that the evidence for lower costs with home care was overwhelming. Meanwhile, another reviewer who examined only studies with comparison or control groups would find overwhelming evidence in the other direction. Knowing that different types of studies generally lead to different sorts of findings offers guidance for the future. Whoever designs the next study to examine the costs of a home care program can try to incorporate the strengths of both types of designs.

Conclusion

Research synthesis is not a panacea. Each effort faces dilemmas. Perhaps because certain value judgments must be made, such as the weight that must be placed on findings from different research designs, some investigators may be tempted to fall back on traditional narrative reviews. I believe that this would be a mistake. Just because a synthesis turns up conflict or requires a judgment call is not good reason to shoot the messenger. The messenger gives us information that is vital in two ways. First, synthesis points to the features of a treatment or program that seem to matter. Is there a crucial background variable? Does research design matter much? How stable are the findings across a group of studies? Second, synthesis helps us to design the next study. Examining the first ten studies and learning which program features are important and which are not help us to develop an effective research plan for the eleventh study. Findings from a synthesis help to make a study as powerful as possible in answering a specific question or resolving a dilemma. In a world of scarce resources, such targeting is valuable. While any one study is important, the great virtue of synthesis is that it helps to answer questions single studies cannot answer.

References

Anderson, S., Auquier, A., Hauck, W., Oakes, D., Vandaele, W., and Weisberg, H. *Statistical Methods for Comparative Studies.* New York: Wiley, 1980.

Baker, P. J., and Crist, U. L. "Teacher Expectancies: A Review of the Literature." In

R. E. Snow and J. D. Elashoff (Eds.), *Pygmalion Reconsidered*. Worthington, Ohio: Jones, 1971.

Bearman, J. E., Loewenson, R. B., and Gullen, W. H. *Muench's Postulates, Laws, and Corollaries, or Biometricians' Views on Clinical Studies*. Biometrics Note No. 4. Bethesda, Md.: Office of Biometry and Epidemiology, National Eye Institute, National Institute of Health, 1974.

Bissell, J. W. "The Effects of Preschool Programs for Disadvantaged Children." Unpublished doctoral dissertation, Harvard University, 1970.

Campbell, D. T., and Erlebacher, A. "How Regression Artifacts in Quasi-Experimental Evaluations Can Mistakenly Make Compensatory Education Look Harmless." In J. Hellmuth (Ed.), *The Disadvantaged Child*. Vol. 3: *Compensatory Education — A National Debate*. New York: Brunner/Mazel, 1970.

Chalmers, T. C. "The Randomized Controlled Trial as a Basis for Therapeutic Decisions." In J. M. Lachin, N. Tygstrup, and E. Juhl (Eds.), *The Randomized Clinical Trial and Therapeutic Decisions*. New York: Marcel Dekker, 1982.

Cicirelli, V. *The Impact of Head Start: An Evaluation of the Effects of Head Start on Children's Cognitive and Affective Development*. Washington, D.C.: Clearinghouse for Federal Scientific and Technical Information, 1969. (ED 036 321)

Datta, L. "The Impact of the Westinghouse/Ohio Evaluation on the Development of Project Head Start." In C. C. Abt (Ed.), *The Evaluation of Social Programs*. Beverly Hills, Calif.: Sage, 1976.

Datta, L. "A Tale of Two Studies: The Westinghouse/Ohio Evaluation of Head Start and the Consortium for Longitudinal Studies Report." *Studies in Educational Evaluation*, 1983, *3*, 271–280.

Edgington, E. S. "An Additive Model for Combining Probability Values from Independent Experiments." *Journal of Psychology*, 1972, *80*, 351–363.

Elashoff, J. D., and Snow, R. E. (Eds.). *Pygmalion Reconsidered*. Worthington, Ohio: Jones, 1971.

Fisher, R. A. *Statistical Methods for Research Workers*. London: Oliver & Boyd, 1973.

Gilbert, J. P., Light, R. J., and Mosteller, F. "Assessing Social Innovation: An Empirical Base for Policy." In C. A. Bennett and A. A. Lumsdaine (Eds.), *Evaluation and Experiment*. New York: Academic Press, 1975.

Glass, G. V. "Integrating Findings: The Meta-Analysis of Research." In L. S. Shulman (Ed.), *Review of Research in Education*. Vol. 5. Itasca, Ill.: Peacock, 1977.

Glass, G. V., McGaw, B., and Smith, M. L. *Meta-Analysis in Social Research*. Beverly Hills, Calif.: Sage, 1981.

Hoaglin, D. C., Light, R. J., McPeek, B., Mosteller, F., and Stoto, M. *Data for Decisions*. Cambridge, Mass.: Abt Books, 1982.

Hunter, J. E., Schmidt, F. L., and Jackson, G. B. *Meta-Analysis: Cumulating Research Findings Across Studies*. Beverly Hills, Calif.: Sage, 1982.

Kohl, H. "Great Expectations." In R. E. Snow and J. D. Elashoff (Eds.), *Pygmalion Reconsidered*. Worthington, Ohio: Jones, 1971.

Light, R. J. "Capitalizing on Variation: How Conflicting Research Findings Can Be Helpful for Policy." *Educational Researcher*, 1979, *8* (8), 3–8.

Light, R. J., and Smith, P. V. "Accumulating Evidence: Procedures for Resolving Contradictions Among Different Research Studies." *Harvard Educational Review*, 1971, *41*, 429–471.

Mosteller, F., and Bush, R. "Selecting Quantitative Techniques." In G. Lindzey (Ed.), *Handbook on Social Psychology*. Vol. 1: *Theory and Method*. Cambridge, Mass.: Addison-Wesley, 1954.

National Academy of Sciences. *Evaluation of the Comprehensive Employment and Training Act*. Washington, D.C.: National Academy Press, 1978.

National Academy of Sciences. *Case Studies of CETA*. Washington, D.C.: National Academy Press, 1979.

Pillemer, D. B., and Light, R. J. "Synthesizing Outcomes: How to Use Research Evidence from Many Studies." *Harvard Educational Review,* 1980, *50,* 176–195.
Raudenbush, S. W. "Utilizing Controversy as a Source of Hypotheses for Meta-Analysis: The Case of Teacher Expectancy's Effects on Pupil IQ." *Journal of Educational Psychology,* forthcoming.
Riecken, H. W., and others. *Social Experimentation: A Method for Planning and Evaluating Social Intervention.* New York: Academic Press, 1974.
Rivlin, A. *Systematic Thinking for Social Action.* Washington, D.C.: Brookings Institution, 1971.
Rosenthal, R., and Jacobson, L. *Pygmalion in the Classroom.* New York: Holt, Rinehart and Winston, 1968.
Ruopp, R., Travers, J., Glantz, F., and Coelen, C. *Children at the Center: Report of the National Daycare Study.* Cambridge, Mass.: Abt Books, 1979.
Ryan, W. *Blaming the Victim.* New York: Pantheon, 1971.
Smith, M. S., and Bissell, J. "Report Analysis: The Impact of Head Start." *Harvard Eduational Review,* 1970, *40,* 51–104.
U.S. General Accounting Office. *The Elderly Should Benefit from Expanded Home Health Care but Increasing Those Services Will Not Ensure Cost Reductions.* Washington, D.C.: U.S. General Accounting Office, 1982.
U.S. General Accounting Office. *WIC Evaluations Provide Some Favorable but No Conclusive Evidence.* Washington, D.C.: U.S. General Accounting Office, 1984.
Winer, B. J. *Statistical Principles in Experimental Design.* New York: McGraw-Hill, 1971.

Richard J. Light is professor at the Graduate School of Education and the Kennedy School of Government at Harvard University, and chairman of the Evaluation Seminar at Harvard. His recent writings emphasize how different forms of statistical evidence can inform policy decisions.

Evaluation synthesis is a form of meta-analysis developed by the U.S. General Accounting Office as a strategy for increasing congressional use of evaluative findings.

Evaluation Synthesis for the Legislative User

Eleanor Chelimsky
Linda G. Morra

The problem of evaluation use is hardly new (Abt, 1978; Alkin and others, 1979; Chelimsky, 1977; Cronbach and others, 1980; Leviton and Hughes, 1981; Pelz, 1978; Rich, 1977; Weiss, 1977; Weiss and Bucuvalas, 1977). There are, of course, many different potential users of evaluations — for example, executive agency decision makers at various levels; legislative authorization, appropriations, and oversight policy makers with their staffs; budget preparers and users in both executive and legislative branches; program practitioners; the evaluation research community; and so forth. Each of these users has an individual perspective — based on position, need, and function — and that perspective must be considered by those who conduct evaluation research if they wish their findings to be used.

One mission of the Program Evaluation and Methodology Division (PEMD) at the U.S. General Accounting Office (GAO) is to improve the use of evaluation by legislators. As part of this effort, we tried, first, to understand the legislative perspective; second, to obtain as clear an idea as possible of legislators' information needs; and third, to develop evaluation strategies that build linkages of logic with those information needs and linkages of communication between evaluators and congressional staff. In this chapter, we focus on one of the PEMD's evaluation strategies, a form of meta-evaluation that we

W. H. Yeaton, P. M. Wortman (Eds.). *Issues in Data Synthesis.*
New Directions for Program Evaluation, no. 24. San Francisco: Jossey-Bass, December 1984.

call *evaluation synthesis.* In order to help the reader to understand this approach, we first describe the legislative perspective and the legislative information needs that contributed to its development. Then, we describe the approach itself and its strengths and limitations.

The Legislative Perspective

In the normal course of events, legislators and researchers are separated by different goals, different standards of evidence, and different tolerances for uncertainty. Researchers have a goal of knowledge or truth; legislators have a goal of power or impact (Price, 1965). Researchers attempt to reach their goal via the scientific method, and both goal and method lead researchers, first, to believe in rational solutions to dilemmas and, second, to define uncertainty very carefully. In contrast, the power goal of legislators is implemented via the adversary process, which leads legislators to believe that the best solution is the one presented with the most persuasive arguments or the one backed up by the most impressive authority (Beranek, 1979). That is, for the legislator, the evidence is instrumental to the negotiation or to the decision, whereas for the researcher, the evidence is an end in itself.

A few years ago, the National Science Foundation (NSF) studied the transfer of evaluative scientific information between researchers and legislators in forty-two states. Researchers worked directly for legislators. During the course of this collaborative effort, problems arose that seemed to be directly attributable to differences of perspective between the two. As one researcher (Beranek, 1979) explained it, "The researcher says he's certain only when he's absolutely certain. To him, making no statement is better than making a statement based on incomplete data. But, in policy making, positive value is placed on 'making a decision,' regardless of whether or not there is sufficient objective evidence to support the decision. . . . In order to make a timely decision based on the best evidence available, certainty to a policy maker can be what a scientist might conjecture as either damn likely or almost never."

Further, these differences in goals and methods between legislators and researchers naturally bring differences in priorities and strategies. As a result, researchers may see the need for research everywhere, and legislators may not see it anywhere. A Minnesota legislator involved in the same NSF study (Voss, 1979) pointed out that legislative priorities exist in the following order: first, constituents; second, legislative feasibility; third, substantive information. What do such legislative priorities signify for the evaluator? If the year's constituent or program issues include, say, fraud or waste in entitlement programs, cost growth in government, poor management, "useless" programs, and program ineffectiveness or inefficiency, in that order, it is clear that evaluation researchers tend to spend most of their time on the least emotional issues and to address the least urgent legislative priorities.

The low legislative priority placed on substance is reinforced by the typically legal, rather than scientific, training of lawmakers and often of their staffs as well. As a result, legislators are generally not familiar with research modes and procedures. This serves to deepen the gulf between legislators and researchers and to make the use of research by legislative bodies even more difficult.

Relationships between researchers and legislators, then, are conditioned not only by different training, different goals, different methods, and different priorities but also and especially by different areas of ignorance. And, the researcher is usually as ignorant of the policy context in which a research question is posed as the legislator is of researcher methods. Yet, to answer the question, Is benzene dangerous? the researcher must know the context in which that question is being asked. Similarly, to use evaluation findings properly, the legislator must know (and care about) the confidence that can be placed in those findings and how they should be applied.

To sum up, it seemed to us at the GAO that an effort to improve the use of evaluative research by legislators must address two kinds of problems: first, the inattention by researchers or evaluators to the information needs and priorities of legislators; second, the communication problems created by the different perspectives of researchers and legislators.

Legislative Information Needs

What are the most common legislative information needs that evaluative techniques can satisfy? To answer this question, we used GAO, Congressional Research Service, and other congressional sources and conducted some interviews of our own as well. The impression we derived was that there are at least six important ways in which evaluators can respond usefully to the needs of legislators and legislative staff. The first way is not only by answering evaluative questions but also by getting the information to the legislative user rapidly enough to fit the time contraints of the congressional negotiation or decision-making process. The second way is by sifting through the quantities of existing evaluative information to synthesize, analyze, and present succinctly that which is relevant to the question at hand. The third way is by refining the formulation of that question so as to be sure of two things: the feasibility of obtaining the information sought and the appropriateness of that information to the policy need. Identifying major gaps in available information for future attention by evaluators is the fourth way. The fifth way is by evaluating plans for new program or policies and reviewing evaluation reports for old ones. The sixth way is by helping congressional staff to develop the evaluative questions about program effectiveness and efficiency to which answers are needed for the legislative oversight, authorization, and budget processes.

To fill these most important kinds of legislative information needs, the GAO has developed some evaluation strategies that build linkages of logic and of communication with the congressional users of its work. These linkages rest on two assumptions: first, that designing backward from the information needed is both feasible and likely to ensure the relevance, timeliness, and use of the work performed; second, that the appropriateness of the evaluation design to the kind of information needed is more important than the sophistication or complexity of that design. One of the resulting strategies is *evaluation synthesis* (U.S. GAO, 1983). The evaluation synthesis addresses all the legislative information needs presented here, but it places particular emphasis on the first four.

The Evaluation Synthesis

The evaluation synthesis represents a cluster of techniques that allows questions about a federal program to be developed collaboratively with congressional committee staff and existing studies that address those questions to be identified, collected, assessed for quality, and, based on the research of the evidence supporting the findings, used as a data base in answering the questions. The end product is distilled information about the state of knowledge on the particular questions at a particular time.

By bringing together existing studies in this way and by using them as a data base in efforts to answer specific congressional questions, synthesis makes it possible to determine what is presently known about a particular topic, the level of confidence that one can place in the individual studies, and the gaps in evaluative information that still remain. Evaluation synthesis may be indicated when congressional committee staff ask for a study of the effectiveness of a federal program, but there are only nine months in which to produce it; when there are major conflicts in the findings produced by different studies of the same program, and committee staff seek explanations for these differences (Chapter Four in this volume discusses this point in some detail); or when the legislature asks for a summary of the state of the evaluative art in a particular topical area. This approach does not claim to produce evaluations faster; instead, it addresses the problem of timeliness by making use of existing evaluations. Evaluation synthesis is a methodology for addressing only those questions that can be answered satisfactorily without conducting primary data collection; it is not a replacement for original data collection.

The evaluation synthesis has several features that distinguish it from the many other efforts involving the review and analysis of evaluative literature. One unusual feature of evaluation synthesis is that, as part of the overall legislative strategy just outlined, it is designed backward from the end use. That is, the evaluation synthesis is driven not by the researcher's general goal of increased knowledge but by a specific congressional need for certain information. This means that the work does not begin with a topic known to be ideal for meta-analysis and with a data base already circumscribed and known to the researcher, whose job is to ask what new information can be derived from the studies that was not available from them individually. Instead, because the question that initiates the evaluation synthesis originates not in the studies themselves but in the Congress, the work must always start with a framework of questions that impart logical cohesion to the effort and that are developed iteratively with the data base. Second, as much emphasis is placed on identifying the gaps in knowledge as in describing what is known about the topic at issue. Some of the questions with which the work starts may be answerable by studies identified during the iterative process, but others may not, and these serve to identify gaps in the desired array of information. Third, the evaluation synthesis is designed systematically to control for bias both in the studies and on the part of the analyst. Fourth, it allows secondary analyses to be performed as needed. Fifth, it emphasizes the importance of nonquantitative analysis.

The evaluation synthesis approach has been documented in the Methods Paper Series of the GAO's Program Evaluation and Methodology Division (PEMD) (U.S. GAO, 1983). There are eight basic steps: identifying and negotiating the study topic and questions, collecting evaluation and other information, determining the types of studies to include, reviewing the studies, redetermining the appropriateness of the synthesis method, synthesizing the information and determining confidence levels, identifying gaps in the evaluative knowledge that remain, and presenting the findings. The first five steps develop through an iterative refining process. PEMD has published four evaluation syntheses to date (U.S. GAO, 1981, 1982a, 1982b, 1982d). More are being prepared. In the following sections, we use the completed syntheses to illustrate the eight steps of the evaluation synthesis and to highlight its distinctive features.

Identifying and Negotiating the Study Topic and Questions. As previously indicated, the evaluation synthesis was developed with the goal of building in linkages of logic and communication with the congressional users of our work. A key element in assuring both linkages is the initial negotiating process during which legislative evaluation sponsors and PEMD staff reach understanding and agreement on the question or questions to be asked, on the appropriateness of the evaluation synthesis to producing the kind of information needed, on the date of its production and availability, and on the use to which the findings will be put.

A series of meetings is held so that we can be reasonably sure that the question can be answered with extant data and that it does not require original data collection, that the question has been framed so that it can be answered with the time and resources available, that the information produced will provide the users with findings of an acceptable degree of conclusiveness given the use envisioned for it, and that the users know exactly what the limitations of the information will be and agree that the information is what they need and want.

What questions can the evaluation synthesis be used to answer? In the PEMD, we have used evaluation synthesis to answer congressional questions about how programs are working—both how programs are operating and what their effects are. For example, we have found that evaluation synthesis can be used to estimate how many people are actually receiving program services. Our report on the Education of All Handicapped Children Act (U.S. GAO, 1981) used fourteen existing studies and two data bases to estimate and describe the number of eligible handicapped children receiving special education services. This report was able to use different sources not only to provide an estimate of how many children were receiving services but also to provide estimates of the children's racial or ethnic background and the severity of their handicaps. No one study provided estimates of each kind, nor did multiple estimates necessarily agree.

We have also used evaluation synthesis to determine how many people need a program service. Our special education report (U.S. GAO, 1981) again serves as an example. The existing studies that we collected and analyzed allowed us to estimate which handicapping conditions were underrepresented and grade and age levels where underrepresentation was notable.

In addition to answering questions about program operations like those just outlined, we have used evaluation synthesis to answer questions about program effects. Our report on the Comprehensive Employment and Training Act (CETA) (U.S. GAO, 1982a), for example, examined the effects of CETA programs on disadvantaged adult enrollees. That report was able to provide legislative users with estimates of wages earned and time employed, public benefits received, and private sector employment of CETA participants before and after they took part in the program. Estimates were also provided for participants' experiences by type of CETA service received. Follow-up reports from the Continuous Longitudinal Manpower Survey provided the data base.

Another PEMD report (U.S. GAO, 1982b) used the evaluation synthesis method to provide estimates of the effectiveness of expanded home health care services for the elderly. Estimates of effect were provided for institutional use, client outcomes, and cost. Twelve major studies were used in determining the estimates. (Chapter Four in this volume discusses that study in some detail.)

We also have used evaluation synthesis to examine the comparative performance of two or more programs. For example, our report on block grants (U.S. GAO, 1982d) addressed the question of whether the poor and other disadvantaged groups have been served equally under block grants and categorical programs. Eight basic evaluation studies—some comprising a series of reports—were used.

Collecting Evaluation and Other Information. While the process used to develop the questions asked in the evaluation ensures its policy relevance, it is not always easy to identify the appropriate universe of studies. (Chapter One in this volume addresses that issue.) While the federal agency that administers the given policy or program is a natural place to begin, we also search for literature that the agency has not sponsored, whether it is published (for example, journal articles) or unpublished (for example, dissertations). Without such a search, it will not be clear how large a part of the universe of relevant studies has been obtained or how biased the retrieved sample may be. Ensuring that no major studies have been omitted is usually a considerable problem in an evaluation synthesis. One approach that we have found useful in preventing such omissions and that we now require is to seek assistance from outside experts both in identifying the literature and in reviewing the studies collected.

Determining the Types of Studies to Include. Once the relevant literature has been identified and collected, the question becomes, What types of studies should the synthesis include? (Chapter Three in this volume addresses this issue.) We have mentioned that one major feature of evaluation synthesis is a deliberate and systematic effort to identify and control potential sources of bias. Toward that end, we view variation in study types as an asset in performing an evaluation synthesis, and, where possible, we make sure that different types of study designs are represented in the synthesis. Our experience suggests that different types of studies can produce different outcomes simply because they have been designed to elicit different kinds of information. Correspondingly, if only one type of study is included, the studies may share a common source of bias, and the synthesis as a whole may take on that bias.

The PEMD's completed synthesis on special education (U.S. GAO, 1981) illustrates the variety of study types that can be included. The data used for that synthesis came from national surveys, case studies, document reviews, and administrative population counts of children receiving special education. We included nonquantitative, process-oriented studies as well as more traditional studies of outcomes or impacts.

Reviewing the Studies. Evaluation synthesis requires an assessment of the overall soundness of each individual study. Because many studies included in an evaluation synthesis present too little statistical information for traditional quantitative synthesis, major weaknesses of study design, conduct, analysis, or reporting that can affect the reliability or validity of each study's findings must be considered. All studies included in a synthesis should be assessed against basic standards for research design, conduct, analysis, and reporting. These criteria should be made explicit and systematically applied to each study in the synthesis. Requiring systematic application of explicit criteria can help control for reviewer bias in assessing the strengths and weaknesses of studies. It prevents a situation in which different reviewers use different criteria and apply them in some instances and not in others.

The application of these criteria should lead to an overall judgment of each study in the synthesis. The consistency or reliability of judgments of study quality is, however, an issue of particular concern. Stock and others (1982) demonstrate the difficulties that it can raise. We believe that, at a minimum, evaluation synthesis should raise the reliability of summary judgments of studies. An approach that we took in our special education synthesis was to include the actual review of each study in a technical appendix. Thus, the reader can assess the basis for the judgment.

Redetermining the Appropriateness of the Synthesis Method. Although preliminary evidence seems to show that evaluation synthesis can answer the question, it sometimes proves that this is not so. For example, we collected a number of studies that attempted to estimate the size of the illegal alien population in the United States (U.S. GAO, 1982c). However, the range in estimates was so enormous, the quality of studies was so questionable, and the potential explanatory factors were so numerous that we concluded that a new research effort would be needed in order to answer the question. Thus, while we believe that the evaluation synthesis can answer many congressional questions, it is no panacea. As a result, we recommend that after a review of the available evidence but before conducting a detailed synthesis, the appropriateness of the synthesis method should be explicitly redetermined.

Synthesizing the Information and Determining Confidence Levels. After a usable set of studies has been assembled, we must next determine how the studies themselves can be compared. No single approach works in all cases. However, we have found that two major factors influence how the studies are compared. First, different evaluative questions are likely to require different approaches for synthesizing the information. Second, the nature of the study designs themselves limits the analyses that are possible. For example, in examining how well a program is working, the question can be, Whom does the program serve under ideal circumstances? Alternatively, the question can be, Whom does the program serve on the average? In the first instance, the analyst may want to investigate a number of case studies and provide a narrative description of the findings. In the second instance, the analyst may calculate an arithmetic average for the answers given by the individual studies, or the analyst may express the answer as the range between the highest and lowest answers. The analysis will be more quantitative in the second case than it is in the first.

Evaluation systems can use the recently developed quantitative approaches for combining the findings of experimental or quasi-experimental studies that rely on statistically based aggregation techniques. (These approaches are described in Chapter Two.) To date, however, the PEMD has been able to use any of these quantitative approaches in only one synthesis (U.S. GAO, 1984). In fact, we do not expect that those techniques will be used in much GAO work, both because of the policy-driven nature of the questions that we must answer and because of the disparate, fragmented, and nontechnical nature of the evaluations that we encounter. While the researcher who selects a topic for synthesis for its new knowledge potential can often use the new statistical approaches, they are usually difficult to apply when designing backward from a congressional committee's question.

Our block grant work (U.S. GAO, 1982d) illustrates this problem quite clearly. There, the PEMD was asked to use existing data to examine administrative costs before and after individual programs were consolidated into block grants. The calculation of comprehensive and reliable estimates of effect was hindered, however, by differing definitions of administrative activities and other accounting procedures, inadequacy in data collection procedures, and weaknesses in sampling. The studies had to be treated in a nonstatistical manner if they were to be useful for informing policy.

The main approach used by the PEMD in evaluation synthesis has been to compare and contrast the studies and their findings. Compared with the traditional statistical approaches, this approach is largely nonquantitative. In comparing the studies, we look for the nature and extent of similar findings or trends across studies and try to rule out competing alternative explanations for the findings. We ask three key questions: What factors lower our confidence, even if findings are similar across studies? What factors, if any, might increase our confidence in the findings across the studies? To what extent can we place confidence in the findings? In contrasting the studies, we focus on exceptions and conflicts. We try to identify study characteristics that might result in outcome variations. These characteristics can suggest tentative hypotheses for further investigation.

We use many nonquantitative ways to compare and contrast the studies and their findings. Pillemer and Light (1980) have identified ways that help us to understand why study outcomes differ. For example, we can ask whether a set of programs with the same name do in fact provide the same services. Some program variations may be more effective than others. We can look for setting-by-treatment interactions, since the effectiveness of a given treatment can vary with who participates in it, where it is administered, or some other situational factor.

Investigating different research designs used across studies as well as different research characteristics of similar designs used across studies can also be indicated. For example, in the special education synthesis (U.S. GAO, 1981), we found that different research designs often provided complementary findings. This increased our confidence in those findings. For instance, both survey and case study findings showed that males were numerically overrepresented in special education classes. However, the case studies also described process-oriented aspects of the program that could explain those findings. Case studies of local school districts suggested that bias in child referral and assessment practices was one possible explanation, and we highlighted this hypothesis for further investigation. Other synthesists (for example, Leifer and others, 1974, who studied the effects of television violence on children) have demonstrated the need to look across studies with similar designs to determine whether such program characteristics as the point in program implementation when researchers conduct their research influence their findings. Chapter Four in this volume discusses these points in some detail.

We may also compare and contrast the studies and their findings in terms of analysis strategies. Even if all the analyses are performed correctly, the particular analysis procedures that are used may be related to findings and create artificial conflicts. For example, conducting an analysis at the pupil, class, or school level can influence estimates of the strength of relationships in evaluations (Haney, 1974).

Problems with study quality that affect our confidence in the study findings can also be used to explain findings. For example, conflicting findings can be resolved if it turns out that one study has been soundly designed and implemented, whereas another has been inappropriately designed for the questions that it seeks to answer.

Even when studies can be statistically synthesized, we have come to believe that they should not be used alone but hand in hand with nonquantitative approaches, since the merging of quantitative and nonquantitative techniques has four important benefits. First, multiple lines of evidence that yield complementary findings provide a stronger research conclusion, in the sense that they enable us to place greater confidence in the findings. Essentially, a cross-validation has been achieved.

Second, studies that cannot be included in the traditional quantitative synthesis—case studies, nonquantitative aggregate studies, expert judgments, process-oriented studies—can help to explain quantitative findings. At a minimum, they can suggest possible explanations, which can then be treated as hypotheses. For example, a statistical synthesis may find that overall a certain program is not effective. However, other studies excluded from the synthesis because their methods were different may provide clues to reasons for the ineffectiveness. These other studies can also play an important role in identifying hypotheses that may explain weak relationships found through statistical synthesis.

Third, quantitative studies contain a great deal of important nonquantitative information. In preparing a study report, researchers and evaluators do not simply list numerical results. The treatment and participants are carefully described, and caveats or limitations are painstakingly laid out. It does not seem to us always either appropriate or desirable to reduce a study to one or several numerical indices. A single number often cannot be interpreted accurately unless we also take into account such factors as subject attrition, changes in study procedures, and other happenings that become major study limitations.

Fourth, in looking at studies comparing people who receive a treatment with others who do not, it may be very important to look at the data from a nonquantitative perspective. One excellent example comes from a study by Fosburg and Glantz (1981). These authors reviewed a series of studies of children's nutrition programs sponsored by the U.S. Department of Agriculture. The simplest quantitative analysis would have involved computing an effect size for each study comparing the health of children who received food supplements with those who did not and then averaging findings across the studies. But, nonquantitative information included in many of the individual studies convinced these authors that that would be fruitless. While for administrative purposes the treatment was the same in each study, information about plate waste (food not eaten) in the nutrition supplements suggested important differences among sites. In some cases, the plate waste was high; other studies reported almost none. In every case, these data were informal and descriptive. But, the reviewers decided that they were crucial. In this setting, combining treatments that had the same administrative name would have amounted in fact to combining groups that received vastly different treatments.

The same dilemma arose for the control groups. They were not all the "pure" no-treatment control groups described in textbooks. Many studies reported that children at sites not receiving assistance from the Department of Agriculture were receiving some food assistance under Title XX of the Social Security Act. This title provides various forms of aid to low-income families. So, control groups in some of the studies in the review were actually quite heavily treated, while others were in fact pure control groups in the sense that they received no food assistance at all.

In this case, the qualitative descriptions of what actually happened to children in the treatment and control groups of each study led the analysts to reorganize their synthesis into subgroups. These subgroups recognized differences between treated and untreated groups that would otherwise have been ignored.

Identifying Gaps and Presenting the Findings. Documenting the fact that questions posed by the Congress cannot be answered with the available evidence has major importance for the evaluation synthesis. In addition to pointing out areas where evaluative efforts may be needed, the evaluation synthesis also helps policy makers to assess the completeness and the reliability of the information on which policy decisions must be based. In our reports for Congress, individual chapters correspond to congressional questions. For each question, we highlight both what is known and what is not known.

Strengths and Limitations of Evaluation Synthesis

Throughout this chapter, we have identified many advantages of the evaluation synthesis approach. This section summarizes the major strengths and identifies the limitations.

Strengths. The major strength of the evaluation synthesis lies in its ability to provide relatively inexpensive, comprehensive, and timely information to the Congress. At the GAO, evaluation synthesis is performed by one or two persons, combining methodological and substantive expertise, over a period of three to nine months. By integrating findings from completed studies, evaluation synthesis can serve congressional needs for relatively short-term evaluative information tailored to specific congressional policy concerns.

Evaluation synthesis directs large amounts of existing and possibly conflicting information from a variety of sources and time periods into a common knowledge base that can be used to answer specific questions. It can increase the power of individual study findings, in that confidence in a given finding is greater if it is the finding of a number of well-done studies than if it is the finding of a single well-done study. Conversely, when studies are not well designed and executed, the knowledge that there is no firm basis for action is also an important benefit to the Congress. The size of the risk in basing policy on uncertain information is clarified, caution is introduced into the debate, and it seems reasonable to expect that over the long term the number of ill-advised legislative program initiatives should diminish.

In setting out what is known and what is not known about the topic, evaluation synthesis also identifies a research agenda that can fill the gaps in needed information and lay the groundwork for further GAO evaluation or audit work. Synthesis also enables legislators to make initial or secondary legislative use of evaluations that have already been completed. In fact, it enables evaluations to be used even though the question at hand may have been a secondary rather than a primary focus of these studies.

Inclusion of nonquantitative studies and of nonquantitative information from quantitative studies is one of evaluation synthesis's most important strengths. Studies of single cases, nonquantitative aggregate studies, quantitative studies that provide too little information for statistical synthesis, narrative reviews of collections of research studies, and other expert judgments are included in an evaluation synthesis when they are available. Omission of these types of studies can cause critically important information to be lost. The same can be said for omission of nonquantitative information from quantitative studies.

Another major strength of the evaluation synthesis approach lies in its deliberate emphasis on controlling for bias in study design and conduct. This emphasis is evident in the systematic eight-step approach and in the inclusion of all relevant literature.

Finally, we have found that evaluation synthesis can also serve, to a limited extent, as a check on the quality of the evaluations performed for a particular program. The technical review of each study included in the synthesis identifies methodological strengths and weaknesses that influence its usefulness. Such review can also influence a sponsor's posture with regard to studies that may be undertaken in the future.

Limitations. The limitations of the evaluation synthesis approach stem from its reliance on extant data. The approach is best applied to areas in which there is a substantial base of evaluation information. Policy concerns for which there is little study information cannot be satisfactorily investigated by this method.

However, even if the information base is substantial, evaluation synthesis is limited in that it can only answer questions that have been addressed by the existing studies. Thus, evaluation synthesis findings are not always generalizable, depending on the nature of the relevant studies and on their quality.

Evaluation synthesis is also limited by poor reporting. As noted in the preceding section, study procedures are sometimes described so summarily that judgments cannot be made about the study's technical adequacy. Moreover, in experimental or quasi-experimental studies, treatments are sometimes so minimally described that the similarities and differences across studies cannot be determined. Still another problem caused by poor reporting is that variables of interest may not be reported consistently across studies. Some studies may report such demographic data as sex, age, and education, while other studies that focus on the same questions do not. Evaluation synthesis is limited by the form and quality of the reports that it uses.

Finally, an evaluation synthesis is only as current as the studies that it analyzes. If studies are several years old, they may identify problems that program managers have already taken steps to address and that no longer characterize the program. Thus, evaluation synthesis is no substitute for primary data collection, but it is useful when questions can be answered with information from existing studies and when time is short.

Conclusion

Evaluation synthesis plays an important role in the PEMD's overall strategy for increasing the use of evaluative findings by the Congress. The shape of this strategy — focused as it is on the information needs of users rather than on the evaluative interests of producers — has evolved from an effort to address the problems encountered by legislative users and evaluators in the past.

The strategy is based on the belief that routinization of the two kinds of linkages that we have discussed — setting up direct and logical ties between the evaluation and the user's needs and ensuring continuous communication between sponsor and evaluator — has four benefits: It increases the relevance and timeliness of the evaluation product, it increases the legislator's understanding of the evaluative process itself, it increases the legislator's satisfaction with evaluation's product, and it increases congressional use of evaluative findings — all with no reduction in evaluative quality.

References

Abt, C. C. (Ed.). *Perspectives on the Costs and Benefits of Applied Social Research*. Cambridge, Mass.: Council for Applied Social Research, 1978.

Alkin, M. C., Daillak, R., and White, P. *Using Evaluation*. Beverly Hills, Calif.: Sage, 1979.

Beranek, W., Jr. "Choosing and Using Scientific Advice in the State Legislature." Presentation to the Conference on Integration and Use of Research Within the Federal

System, Operations Research Society of America/The Institute of Management Science, Hawaii, June 1979.

Chelimsky, E. *An Analysis of the Proceedings of a Symposium on the Use of Evaluation by Federal Agencies.* McLean, Va.: Mitre Corporation, 1977.

Cronbach, L. J., Ambron, S. R., Dornbusch, S. M., Hess, R. D., Hornik, R. C., Phillips, D. C., Walker, D. F., and Weiner, S. S. *Toward Reform of Program Evaluation: Aims, Methods, and Institutional Arrangements.* San Francisco: Jossey-Bass, 1980.

Fosburg, S., and Glantz, F. *Analysis Plan for the Childcare Food Program.* Cambridge, Mass.: Abt Associates, 1981.

Haney, W. *Units of Analysis Issues in the Evaluation of Project Follow Through.* Cambridge, Mass.: Huron Institute, 1974.

Leifer, A., Gordon, N., and Graves, S. "Children's Television: More Than Mere Entertainment." *Harvard Educational Review,* 1974, *44,* 213–245.

Leviton, L. C., and Hughes, E. F. "Research on the Utilization of Evaluations." *Evaluation Review,* 1981, *5,* 525–548.

Pelz, D. C. "Some Expanded Perspectives on the Use of Social Science in Public Policy." In J. M. Yinger and S. T. Cutter (Eds.), *Major Social Issues: A Multidisciplinary View.* New York: Free Press, 1978.

Pillemer, D. B., and Light, R. J. "Benefiting from Variation in Study Outcomes." In R. Rosenthal (Ed.), *Quantitative Assessment of Research Domains.* New Directions for Methodology of Social and Behavioral Science, no. 5. San Francisco: Jossey-Bass, 1980.

Price, D. K. *The Scientific Estates.* Cambridge, Mass.: Harvard University Press, 1965.

Rich, R. F. "Uses of Social Science Information by Federal Bureaucrats: Knowledge for Action Versus Knowledge for Understanding." In C. H. Weiss (Ed.), *Using Social Research in Public Policymaking.* Lexington, Mass.: Heath, 1977.

Stock, W. A., Okun, M. A., Haring, M. J., Miller, W., and Ceurvorst, R. W. "Rigor in Data Synthesis: A Case Study of Reliability in Meta-Analysis." *Educational Researcher,* 1982, *11,* 10–14.

U.S. General Accounting Office. *Disparities Still Exist in Who Gets Special Education.* Washington, D.C.: U.S. General Accounting Office, 1981.

U.S. General Accounting Office. *CETA Programs for Disadvantaged Adults—What Do We Know About Their Enrollees, Services, and Effectiveness?* Washington, D.C.: U.S. General Accounting Office, 1982a.

U.S. General Accounting Office. *The Elderly Should Benefit from Expanded Home Health Care but Increasing These Services Will Not Ensure Cost Reductions.* Washington, D.C.: U.S. General Accounting Office, 1982b.

U.S. General Accounting Office. *Problems and Options in Estimating the Size of the Illegal Alien Population.* Washington, D.C.: U.S. General Accounting Office, 1982c.

U.S. General Accounting Office. *Lessons Learned from Past Block Grants: Implications for Congressional Oversight.* Washington, D.C.: U.S. General Accounting Office, 1982d.

U.S. General Accounting Office. *The Evaluation Synthesis.* Institute for Program Evaluation Methods Paper I. Washington, D.C.: U.S. General Accounting Office, 1983.

U.S. General Accounting Office. *WIC Evaluations Provide Some Favorable but No Conclusive Evidence on the Effects Expected for the Special Supplemental Programs for Women, Infants, and Children.* Washington, D.C.: U.S. General Accounting Office, 1984.

Voss, G. Panel discussion remarks at the Conference on Integration and Use of Research Within the Federal System, ORSA/TIMS, Hawaii, June 1979.

Weiss, C. H. "Introduction." In C. H. Weiss (Ed.), *Using Social Research in Public Policy Making.* Lexington, Mass.: Heath, 1977.

Weiss, C. H., and Bucuvalas, M. J. "The Challenge of Social Research to Decision Making." In C. H. Weiss (Ed.), *Using Social Research in Public Policy Making.* Lexington, Mass.: Heath, 1977.

Eleanor Chelimsky is director of the Program Evaluation and Methodology Division at the U.S. General Accounting Office. She was president of the Evaluation Research Society in 1981 and received that organization's Myrdal Award for Government in 1982.

Linda G. Morra is a project director and heads the Education, Employment, and Retirement Group for the Program Evaluation and Methodology Division at the U.S. General Accounting Office. She received the Director's Award in 1981 for her work on GAO's first evaluation synthesis.

Index

meta-analysis of quasi-experiments, 5–24; and relative or absolute performance, 65–66; and research design, 68, 70–71; and stability of effectiveness, 67–68; statistical methods for, 25–42; and treatment features, 61–63; treatment type matched with recipient type by, 59–61

T

Takaro, T., 55
Technology assessment, concept of, 43
Teele, J. E., 10, 24
Thompson, M. S., 51, 55
Thomsen, J., 55
Travers, J., 73

U

U.S. Census Bureau, 15n
U.S. Department of Agriculture, 84–85
U.S. Department of Labor, 63
U.S. General Accounting Office (GAO), 1, 3, 67–69, 70, 73, 75–89; Program Evaluation and Methodology Division (PEMD) of, 75, 79–83, 87
U.S. Senate Committee on Agriculture, Nutrition, and Forestry, 67
U.S. Senate Committee on Labor and Human Resources, 70

V

Validity: construct, 7–8; external, 8–9; internal, 11–12; statistical conclusion, 10–11; threats to, 7–12, 18, 53
Vandaele, W., 71
Voss, G., 76, 88

W

Wagner, J. L., 44, 55
Walker, D. F., 22, 88
Weikart study, 60
Weinberg, M., 10, 24
Weiner, S. S., 22, 88
Weisberg, H., 71
Weiss, C. H., 75, 88
West, S. G., 51, 55
Westinghouse Learning Corporation, 59–61
White, P., 87
Williams, W., 6, 23
Winer, B. J., 62, 73
Women, Infants, and Children (WIC), Special Supplemental Program for, interactions in, 67–69
Wortman, P. M., 1–24, 43–56
Wright, B. D., 22

Y

Yeaton, W. H., 1–4, 6, 13, 24, 43–56
Yusuf, S., 51, 55, 56

Z

Zelis, R., 49, 56

1. TITLE OF PUBLICATION	A. PUBLICATION NO.							2. DATE OF FILING
New Directions for Program Evaluation	4	4	9	0	5	0		9/30/84

3. FREQUENCY OF ISSUE	A. NO. OF ISSUES PUBLISHED ANNUALLY	B. ANNUAL SUBSCRIPTION PRICE
quarterly	4	$35 inst/$25 indv

4. COMPLETE MAILING ADDRESS OF KNOWN OFFICE OF PUBLICATION (Street, City, County, State and ZIP Code) (Not printers)

433 California St., San Francisco (SF County), CA 94104

5. COMPLETE MAILING ADDRESS OF THE HEADQUARTERS OR GENERAL BUSINESS OFFICES OF THE PUBLISHERS (Not printers)

433 California St., San Francisco (SF County), CA 94104

6. FULL NAMES AND COMPLETE MAILING ADDRESS OF PUBLISHER, EDITOR, AND MANAGING EDITOR (This item MUST NOT be blank)

PUBLISHER (Name and Complete Mailing Address)

Jossey-Bass Inc., Publishers, 433 California St., S.F., CA 94104

EDITOR (Name and Complete Mailing Address)

Ernest House, CIRCE-270, Univ. of Illinois, Champaign, IL 61820

MANAGING EDITOR (Name and Complete Mailing Address)

William Henry, Jossey-Bass Publishers, 433 California St., S.F., CA 94104

7. OWNER (If owned by a corporation, its name and address must be stated and also immediately thereunder the names and addresses of stockholders owning or holding 1 percent or more of total amount of stock. If not owned by a corporation, the names and addresses of the individual owners must be given. If owned by a partnership or other unincorporated firm, its name and address, as well as that of each individual must be given. If the publication is published by a nonprofit organization, its name and address must be stated.) (Item must be completed)

FULL NAME	COMPLETE MAILING ADDRESS
Jossey-Bass Inc., Publishers	433 California St., S.F., CA 94104

For names and addresses of stockholders, see attached list.

8. KNOWN BONDHOLDERS, MORTGAGEES, AND OTHER SECURITY HOLDERS OWNING OR HOLDING 1 PERCENT OR MORE OF TOTAL AMOUNT OF BONDS, MORTGAGES OR OTHER SECURITIES (If there are none, so state)

FULL NAME	COMPLETE MAILING ADDRESS
Same as #7	

9. FOR COMPLETION BY NONPROFIT ORGANIZATIONS AUTHORIZED TO MAIL AT SPECIAL RATES (Section 411.3, DMM only)
The purpose, function, and nonprofit status of this organization and the exempt status for Federal income tax purposes (Check one)

(1) ☐ HAS NOT CHANGED DURING PRECEDING 12 MONTHS	(2) ☐ HAS CHANGED DURING PRECEDING 12 MONTHS	(If changed, publisher must submit explanation of change with this statement.)

10. EXTENT AND NATURE OF CIRCULATION	AVERAGE NO. COPIES EACH ISSUE DURING PRECEDING 12 MONTHS	ACTUAL NO. COPIES OF SINGLE ISSUE PUBLISHED NEAREST TO FILING DATE
A. TOTAL NO. COPIES (Net Press Run)	3431	3135
B. PAID CIRCULATION 1. SALES THROUGH DEALERS AND CARRIERS, STREET VENDORS AND COUNTER SALES	107	3
2. MAIL SUBSCRIPTION	1643	1410
C. TOTAL PAID CIRCULATION (Sum of 10B1 and 10B2)	1750	1413
D. FREE DISTRIBUTION BY MAIL, CARRIER OR OTHER MEANS SAMPLES, COMPLIMENTARY, AND OTHER FREE COPIES	87	55
E. TOTAL DISTRIBUTION (Sum of C and D)	1837	1468
F. COPIES NOT DISTRIBUTED 1. OFFICE USE, LEFT OVER, UNACCOUNTED, SPOILED AFTER PRINTING	1594	1667
2. RETURN FROM NEWS AGENTS	0	0
G. TOTAL (Sum of E, F1 and 2 - should equal net press run shown in A)	3431	3135

11. I certify that the statements made by me above are correct and complete	SIGNATURE AND TITLE OF EDITOR, PUBLISHER, BUSINESS MANAGER, OR OWNER *John R. Ward* Vice-President

PS Form 3526 July 1981

(See instruction on reverse)

(Page 1)